After Gus

After Gus

Kathryn Glendinning

First published in 2008 by:
STAMFORD HOUSE PUBLISHING

ISBN 978-1-904985-60-0

Printed and bound in Great Britain by:
STAMFORD HOUSE PUBLISHING
Remus House
Coltsfoot Drive
Woodston
Peterborough
PE2 9JX

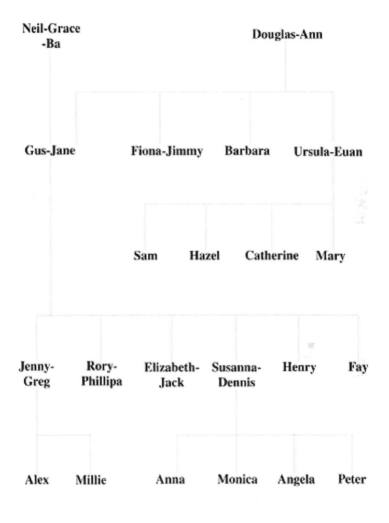

Family Tree

DEDICATION

To

Alistair, James and Malcolm

ACKNOWLEDGEMENTS

I would like to thank Barbara Gilbert for her invaluable help and advice. I am also grateful to Camilla Shelley, Kerry Miller and Pam Hobbes for their assistance and support.

Chapter 1

Gus. He had always been Gus. Gus or Gus Mac, like a drink, whisky mac or Gus Mac, what's your tipple? I must have been a very slow child, for it wasn't until I was about fourteen that I discovered Gus was short for Angus. Rory had brought a friend home from school, one Angus Black. When introduced to my father he had amiably remarked that they shared a name. I understood this cryptic comment; my father was obviously referring to his middle name, Duff, which I'd been told meant black in Gaelic. Angus had no reason to know this fact, so I explained it to him. It was only then that I learnt his name was also my father's name.

As an only child of an Edinburgh doctor, his had been the most conventional of Scottish childhoods. After a private school education there was a short spell in the Marines at the end of the war, short enough for him not to see active service, and immediately after this he went on to Oxford. Rubbing shoulders with the other 'bright sparks' he realized the true value of an Oxford education, acquiring useful contacts, learning to present himself well and achieving his greatest personal triumph, a blue at rugby, as good as a first-class degree to his mind. Just as well, perhaps, as in the event he came down with a third.

He started working in sales for one of the large oil companies in London. Being a provincial boy at heart, he found life in London difficult and lonely. A friend from university told him of a fellow graduate who was working in Aylesbury and missing university life. Gus arranged to visit Jane at her parents' house for Sunday lunch.

Granny told me of all the fuss Jane went to beforehand, cleaning the rooms, planning the menu, the dilemma over the seating arrangements at table and which dress she should wear. Strict instructions were handed out. No one was to argue with Jane, or mention any embarrassing incidents. Under no circumstances was Fiona to flirt with Gus. Barbara and Ursula were to be kept out of the way as much as possible. The preparations completed, Jane headed for the station in a state of great excitement to meet the dashing young man.

Granny's first thought, she told me, as she looked out of the upstairs study window and saw them walking up the drive together was, *poor Jane, what a shame.*

He was completely bald.

Gus didn't stand a chance. Jane was from that group of post war females who, having seen the depletion of Britain's youth, catapulted themselves into early marriages with an unflinching resolve to repopulate the country. Within six months he and Jane were married.

The nature of my father's job at the oil company meant he moved to different offices every eighteen months and every two years a baby was born, me in Shrewsbury, Rory in Leicester, Elizabeth in Romsey, and Susanna in Edinburgh . . .At which point my parents decided they'd had enough. Enough relocating. They wanted to stay in Scotland. So when Gus started a new career in Glasgow with a road haulage company my mother decided she wanted to join the ranks of the landed gentry. There's no harm in wanting to better yourself, so they bought a large house with stables attached, farm buildings two hundred yards down the road and four hundred acres of land. Here Henry was born, then Fay. Six children in eleven years. It was hardly surprising that acquaintances speculated as to our religious convictions.

Torlochan is the name everyone calls the farm, although the proper name is Torlochan Home Farm. Originally, it served to stock the kitchen of Torlochan House and estate, set on the edge of woods. The word woods, like house, now seems a somewhat unpretentious name, for the woods that spread for miles and miles are surely a forest and the house with large oak-panelled halls and dining rooms, a library and servants', quarters along with eighteen bedrooms, is more like a castle. The MacGregors had lived in the house for over two hundred years, selling off bits of land piecemeal to pay off death duties or other debts.

A couple of years after we moved to the farm, the MacGregors decided that, with two children who were uninterested in living in their ancestral home, it was best to throw in the towel and move to Jersey, like a lot of people at that time intent on avoiding Wilson's crippling inheritance tax.

The shopkeeper in the village did have a wicked sense of humour. He told my mother that the house had been bought by the local authority to convert into a Borstal. And a very plausible proposition it was. A large house, three miles from the village, only twenty-odd miles from Glasgow. The outbuildings could easily convert into residences for the staff. It made perfect sense.

"What a nightmare," my mother wailed, "we can't live next door to a Borstal brimming over with the worst type of delinquent. Imagine what they might do to the children, especially the girls. No one will ever want to come and visit us or let their children near the place. We'll have to sell the farm and move somewhere else. And who in their right mind would buy a place right next door to a Borstal? We're going to lose all our money!"

My father's response was more reasonable. He put on his smart tweed jacket and walked down the road to speak to the MacGregors, returning shortly with a broad grin of relief across his face. The house had been sold, not to the local authority, but to a Catholic brotherhood; it would be a training centre for missionaries. The place would be heaving with young men, but not of the type my mother had feared; our virtue was safe after all.

The priests proved to be good neighbours and, on the occasions when my father visited them in the evening to discuss boundary fences or whatever, he discovered that they, like him, had a palate for good malt whisky. They didn't have to get the bottle out of the cupboard when they offered him a drink, it was already on the table, with the top off. At other times, the priests would call at our house to invite us to a whist drive they were organising, or to warn us that there would be an Open Day at the weekend and to expect bus loads of Catholics. So, over the years, we got to know them pretty well. The only trouble with having priests as neighbours was that some of the younger children's friends who came to play could not understand why Henry and Fay had so many fathers.

The original plan was that Jane would manage the farm and its workers on a daily basis with the help of a farm manager and, in the evenings, Gus, who was busy running his company during the day, would do his bit, keeping the accounts and applying for grants and subsidies.

Douglas, Jane's father, tried to dissuade them. After all farming wasn't part of life's natural progression; it wasn't nature, it was nurture. Farmers came from farming families brought up on the land, not suburbia. What did Jane and Gus know of farming? It was a different culture. His words fell on stony ground. Jane's idea of being a farmer had caught hold; her indomitable will was bent on its course. In the perversity of her temperament, she chose to view his well-meant concern as a slight on her competence, her ability.

"Oh ye of little faith." She would show him.

So the conversion commenced. The crusading spirit was out to conquer. She immersed herself in farming life. She read *The Scottish Farmer* and *Farmer's Weekly*. She and my father joined the National Farmer's Union and attended local agricultural shows, learning all they could as they tried to get to grips with the problems of running a dairy. It struck me that all they could talk of was the farm and I sometimes wondered what other families discussed at table if it wasn't mastitis in cows, whether a heifer was in calf or not, or how the dog had managed to get ticks again. One would imagine that this total immersion in matters agricultural would have infused some enthusiasm into me, but, such is my nature, I swore I would never marry a farmer. Now, many years later, I'm beginning to think what pleasure I would have with just a small-holding, perhaps a few sheep and hens, and a cockerel to keep them happy!

Jane became a willing slave to the farm. Seven years as a full-time housewife and mother had left her bored and frustrated. Farming would be an interest for her and my father to share, but the skills of farming and dairy husbandry were not to be so easily mastered, nor were honest, reliable farm workers ten a penny.

So, along with the book-keeping, my father also had to learn the practicalities of dairy farming. Frequently, at the weekends, he'd be in the dairy by 5am, washing the cows' udders, attaching the milking machine, moving the cows in and out of the dairy in batches of eight, and checking they were all being given the correct supplement. When the milking was over he'd sluice out the dairy and clean the yard before attending to the calves and the cows in calf. I saw him once assist a cow with a difficult delivery, rolling up his shirt-sleeve and plunging his hand deep into the cow's innards. After much grunting from both the cow and my father, a pair of tiny feet appeared, followed by the rest of a diminutive animal covered in slime and gore.

Then, on Monday morning, my father would give himself a close shave, polish his shoes, don a pristine white shirt and smart suit, neatly knot his tie and, stepping into his other persona, assume the air of an elegant man-about-town gliding off gracefully in the fashionable company car.

My mother had always had cleaners to help with the housework, but now my parents decided it made more sense economically to employ a live-in child carer to look after us children and for my mother to work on the farm. My parents embarked on employing a series of nannies, as they called them, although I think the term nanny may give the wrong impression. The girls who came, some only for a few months, some for as long as a year, were hardly adults themselves. However, as I remember, they were kind to us on the whole. They showed us how to blow bubbles with bubblegum and how to dance the twist. They told us about their boyfriends and French kissing. I didn't want to believe adults could be so disgusting. Living miles from the nearest town and even further from their relatives, they must have felt lonely, but Jane always made a great fuss of them, grateful for all the help she could get. One young girl from Liverpool, a distant cousin of my mother's, was packed off up to Scotland after having a 'fortunate miscarriage'. I suspect her mother thought a spell looking after so many children would show her the folly of her ways and she would return a reformed character. The stint at Torlochan didn't have the desired effect, for two years later she was the mother of an illegitimate child. There was another nanny called Sandra who wanted to become a midwife and would stay up all hours of the night to watch calves and lambs being born. I think she was our 'nanny' for longer than any other girl. We had a mature nanny called Gladys who stayed in the gamekeeper's cottage with her two sons, one of whom was on probation for shoplifting. She claimed to be a widow, although my mother reckoned her husband was 'in the clink'. One day she didn't turn up for work, so Arnold was dispatched to find out why, only to discover that she and her sons had done a moonlight flit, leaving numerous unpaid bills in their wake.

With the arrival of the first nanny, Jane learnt to drive a tractor. It looked incongruous; this slight, womanly figure perched precariously on the seat of a mechanical monstrosity. With a scarf tied round her head and her bare arms exposed to the elements, she would lean forward, grasping the wheel, as though on horse-back, encouraging the beast with the direction of her body. Up and down the fields she would go, ploughing, spraying on fertilisers, ferrying loads of silage to the silos, whatever the season demanded. She was happy with her new responsibility as farmer out in the open air. She had at last done with the daily drudge of childcare.

Financially and practically my parents had bitten off more than they could chew and Rory and I, aware of our parents' anxiety over money, put our ingenuity to work, convinced that we could find a solution. We collected old fizzy drink bottles from rubbish dumps and bins at picnic areas, washed them and asked my mother to stop by the shop the next time we were passing in the car. Appalled, Mr Petrie the shopkeeper gave us a terrible ticking off. He knew quite well we hadn't bought the bottles from his shop. What were we thinking of?

"But your parents must have plenty of money, buying that big farm. Tinkers, travelling people, people like that; well, they collect old bottles and try to flog them to the shops, but not respectable people." He shook his head in scandalised horror.

"Have you no pride? What would your mother say if she knew?"

Little did he know that she was keen to encourage this entrepreneurial trait. She was sitting outside in the getaway car, waiting for us to appear with the loot in our grubby paws, but we had enough savvy not to tell him that. Our next enterprise was selling brambles, but we couldn't find any purchasers. I remember crying one weekend when my father insisted on giving me my pocket money. I wanted him to keep his money for the farm.

Astonishingly, in the midst of all the financial anxiety, there was a sudden whir of activity on the farm; the buildings were all given a lick of paint, the pot-holes in the road were filled in, the brambles and nettles cut away from the verges to smarten up the road, and the fallen tree behind the house was sawn into logs and stacked neatly. The barns took on a more orderly appearance, as haphazard heaps of bales were tidied up; catches were mended on doors that normally stood ajar and rubbish was carted off to the nearest dump.

My father had decided the business of trying to make ends meet had become too much and at the end of one Sunday lunch he announced he had some bad news and some good news to tell us. First he declared the bad news. "We are going to sell the farm and move to Dollar. It's a very pleasant town and there is a good school there which you children can go to, the one that your cousins are at." At this point my mother burst into bitter tears. One would have thought it was the first she had heard of the plan. She was heart-broken at the realisation that all her hopes and ambitions had come to an end. All her hard work, her sacrifices, her efforts had come to this. During her conversion she had learnt to ridicule town life, she had become a country woman, a farmer, grafted on by hard work and effort. Now she was to be plunged into the heart of all she despised: suburbia and townies.

Chameleon-like, I too burst into tears seeing my mother so upset, aware of the disappointment this brought her, the dashing of her dreams. Like a true crusader, failure had not been an option. Hadn't she told me she was doing all this for us, for her children, and soon it would be someone else's?

"Now don't upset yourself so much, please," my father begged, looking pointedly at Mum. Her tears subsided and so did mine; the other children looked on in a state of shock. It was not unusual to see me shed tears, but my mother weeping was out of character.

"Now for the good news," he asserted. "Round about Christmas time we are going to have another baby."

At this point my mother again burst into uncontrollable wailing. I loved babies; surely my mother loved them too. What was the crying for this time? Hadn't my father said this was the good news?

The following week we were taken to see a large red sandstone house on the outskirts of Dollar, which was within commuting distance of Glasgow, but in almost the opposite direction to Torlochan.

The farm wasn't sold. I suppose it was normal for Grampa to help his only child. He and Ba, my step grandmother, underwrote the debts. The pedigree dairy herd was sold and replaced by beef cows and sheep. The correlation between the dramatic fall in the workload and the reduction of my parents stress levels was palpable.

It was about this time that Arnold and Isabel came to live and work at Torlochan. Arnold was the son of a gamekeeper, brought up on a Highland estate. There had been no work there for the young Arnold, so he'd packed his bags and followed his cousin to the bright lights of Glasgow. He'd trained as a mechanic at Dad's haulage firm and apparently was one of their best. After his marriage to Isabel he'd handed in his notice, telling the foreman he wanted to work on the land, hopefully as a gamekeeper. When my father heard of his career move he offered him work at Torlochan. A godsend, my mother called him, and life did become easier for my parents after his arrival. A mechanic, a gamekeeper and a farm worker all rolled into one, with a wife on the side who doubled up as a cleaner and a cook.

Once again Jane tried to construct an agricultural utopia. If the farm couldn't produce milk it would produce eggs. She bought hens, eleven of them to be precise, and one testosterone-charged cockerel. She was told a cockerel was a promiscuous bird and craved a number of mates to satisfy his desires, and as nature took its course, so the number of hens and cockerels increased. Originally a henhouse was bought and a hen run constructed to contain these birds, but they insisted on escaping. Their wings were duly clipped, they still escaped. My mother was frightened to clip their wings any further lest she amputate part of the wing along with the feathers, so they were given more feed as an

8

inducement to stay within the confines of their official abode. They were a determined lot, however, and finally Jane admitted defeat and allowed them the freedom of the farm. We learnt to play by their rules, leaving 'wally' eggs in the comfortable, sheltered corners of barns and hay sheds, where they would snuggle down making nests for themselves. Here they would sit and cackle and wriggle their bottoms until with a look of great concentration, the egg popped out and there they would leave it beside the counterfeit, oblivious to the conspiracy. Here we children came into our own as we were packed off to search for the day's eggs. When the hens became old and scrawny, or the chickens grew up to be promiscuous males instead of productive females, my mother would summon Arnold and instruct him to do his bit. Nothing tastes as good as free-range poultry.

Even with financial assistance from my grandparents, the cost of having six children to raise and educate privately, whilst always trying to maintain appearances, meant that my parents were never flush with money. Economies had to be made wherever possible.

My mother's sewing skills were put to the test and she made as many of our clothes as she could. Late into the night she would sit over her old Singer sewing machine, her forearm shunting backwards and forwards, backwards and forwards, with all the regularity of a piston. I can see her now in my mind's eye, silhouetted against the wall, her head down, moving in rhythm with her hand, her eyes focused on the cloth, scanning the stitches with all the competence of an experienced seamstress. She altered, patched and made all that she could. Her economising was not limited to clothes; she adapted curtains handed down from relatives and created large patchwork quilt covers from remnants of material. The carpet in the hall had been cut down to size and fitted by her and Isabel, having originally graced my grandparents' sitting room, until it was replaced by an insurance claim when the sparks from a coal fire singed the wool, leaving little black spots radiating out from the hearth. Now the little black spots appeared sporadically along the length of the upstairs hall.

Food was another area where Jane could budget. During the week the evening meals consisted of Welsh Rarebit, Toad in the Hole, baked potatoes or macaroni cheese. Lunch at the weekend, when my father was present, was when meat and two veg appeared on the table. However, she could produce an excellent meal when the need arose, so when we did have guests she'd rustle up an appetising meal and say:

"F.H.B., F.H.B. please." The guests would look bewildered; however, we knew exactly what she meant. The subtext of 'Family hold back' was, "I may have put together a delicious meal but I haven't gone overboard with the quantity, so don't complain if you aren't given as much as you'd like and don't ask for second helpings. If there is any thing left over we'll heat it up and have it tomorrow as a treat."

Our holidays were humble affairs. Children are impressionable and my mother managed to persuade us how exciting a week spent in a caravan park at St. Monans would be. And it was exciting, eating fish and chips out of newspaper for a week. It did have its charms. It was curious seeing the women from the other caravans walking around during the day with their hair wound round like corkscrews in curlers, then in the evening dolling themselves up to play bingo. Curiously, my father often discovered a couple of days into the holiday that there was some crisis or other at the farm and it was imperative that he return immediately, coming back to St. Monans on the final day of the holiday to collect the family.

I suppose, looking back on it, our existence was what the Glaswegians refer to as 'fur jackets and no knickers', although I think Jane would rather allude to our lifestyle as impoverished gentility.

Chapter 2

When Greg, Alex and I arrived at Burnside, Jane's new house, she came down the steps and met me with a warmth she'd never shown before. She hugged me and held me in her arms.

"Don't be sad Jenny; your father wouldn't have wanted that." How could I be anything else?

My family were all there. Greg and I were the last to arrive. Jane had wanted to have a meal with all of us, on this evening, the evening before Gus's funeral. An extra leaf had been put in the dining room table, yet still there was not enough room as we sat elbow to elbow. My mother sat at the head of the table with Ba by her side and Rory sitting at the other end where my father normally sat, occasionally getting up to diligently replenish empty wine glasses, the way my father had done, taking on his new role as head of the family, with Phillipa sitting attentively at his side.

I barely knew his wife. Before today I had only met her twice, at their wedding and a year before that, when they had first become engaged. She was pretty, exceptionally pretty, and there was a kind of easy, serene grace in the way she held herself with a self-assured poise. She dressed with a style that highlighted her loveliness. Her long elegant neck accentuated her natural grace and undulating curves that swept down the whole length of her strong, supple body to legs that seemed to go on for ever. Despite her tender years and hearing disability she had tremendous confidence, slotting into the role of Rory's wife with an artless ease. Her qualities simply served to make me feel gauche. I comforted myself with the thought that only a genetic freak would have such elongated bones.

My mother had been in despair, believing that Rory would never settle down. He enjoyed playing the field, as the saying goes, so when, in his mid-thirties when many of his friends were already packing their children off to boarding schools, Rory finally plumped for Phillipa, my mother was not so much delighted as greatly relieved. Phillipa would not have been her first choice. As a townie she didn't have the 'right' background. Also, there was the small matter of the genetic disability, although hopefully it only went down the female line! Political correctness did not exercise my mother greatly.

"Her mother's only a nursery nurse and her father is some kind of engineer," she told me dismissively. "Rory's only marrying her on the rebound. He should have married Alison; she was much more suitable; her family are sheep farmers in the Borders. She knew all about farming and could have been a tremendous help to Rory, but he just couldn't clinch it."

"Too cavalier," she reckoned. "He's used to girls throwing themselves at his feet; he could treat them as he liked and they came back for more. Alison was different, she expected him to behave correctly and he just didn't know how to play his cards properly. Phillipa, she hasn't a clue about stock-rearing."

"I can see her pedigree's not too good but I'd say she has good child-bearing hips," I commented flippantly, wondering what remarks she'd made about the stock Greg had derived from. "Don't worry. I reckon she'll start popping out lambs of her own in a couple of years."

Now she sat diligently between her husband and Jack. My unmarried sister and brother Fay and Henry were there, along with Susanna and her Californian husband Dennis.

Susanna had made a brilliant marriage and tonight I sat next to Dennis, perfect husband for the perfect daughter. Tall, dark, not handsome, but interesting, he was intelligent and cultured, with a courteous self-confidence. He appeared almost delicate, slightly over sensitive, slightly over enthusiastic, the son of rich Californians and very American. He had the best of everything because that was what he expected and, sitting next to me in dark green corduroy trousers and an ivory shirt, his understated style made me think that he was the very best type of American. I don't know if his parents were pleased about the match but Jane was enraptured with Susanna's choice of husband, and this delight in her son-in-law was largely due to his wealthy connections.

He was sensible to the reason for Jane's preference and it produced a diffidence in his manner towards her. I'd been introduced to his father, Hank, at his wedding, and the word for him was portly. We'd floundered about for something to say, making small talk about the journey to Scotland, when what I wanted to know was *what is it like to be so rich?* Jane had told us that he owned his own executive aeroplane, which, surely even by Californian standards, must be a mark of great wealth.

"It's not like having a car," Greg pointed out, "you can't skip on the maintenance one month if you are feeling the pinch."

Despite the sad circumstances, the meal passed surprisingly pleasantly. Amidst the general hum of conversation, I grumbled to Dennis about the teething troubles I was having settling into our new house. Extricating myself from London was proving more painful than I'd expected. We had recently moved to Henley as a result of Greg's new job in Reading. There was a gap in my life now which I felt would never be filled. I moaned on about the people there; would anyone ever talk to me, would I ever put down roots? I hadn't wanted to leave London and the friends I'd made. Dennis politely retreated to our original topic and told me the reasons for their move, how their expanding family was having trouble fitting into their cottage. "You'll have to come down with Greg and Alex soon, you're the only members of your family not to see it."

I grunted non-committedly. Of my three sisters I liked Susanna the least, whether it was just a clash of personalities or jealously on my part of the obvious favouritism my mother showed towards her. Perhaps in other circumstances I would have been happy to pursue the friendship Dennis showed towards us, for it was difficult not to like him. My attitude to Susanna had not improved over the years. Since her marriage to Dennis, her inflated wealth reinforced Jane's preference for Susanna, heightening the opinion she had of herself. Strangely, I noticed, her vocal cords had moved in sympathy with her social ascendancy, raising the voice that emerged.

Although Mum is looking at Susanna, I know the message is aimed at me.

"There'll be no crying in the church. Do you understand? Your father would not like it. It's alright to cry at the graveyard, but nowhere else."

I remembered how I'd cried at my grandfather's funeral, and I'd never forget my mother's shame. Letting the side down with a public display of grief was a weakness she could not bear. She was adamant, this time there would be no crying. We would all take a valium tablet.

Greg is crying though. He weeps and weeps, grief-stricken at my father's death. He must feel such a prat standing next to Ba. She's doing her dignified restraint act again. Last week, on the way to her solicitor's with my father, she'd watched Dad drop dead at her feet in the middle of George Street. Then, as now, her Calvinistic background stood her in good stead; there was no show of emotion, not even for her stepson.

I look down the steps towards the immense rectangular stone slabs of the small church, and wonder vaguely why people are standing outside in the cold and wet. I smile vacuously, assuming this is the correct thing to do. No one smiles back; they stare at me gloomily. I look at my mother. She isn't smiling either. This isn't the time to smile when there's only sadness in the air.

Entering the church and seeing the pews packed to capacity, I realise that, if the mourners outside had been inside, we would have been unable to make our way with any dignity to the pews reserved for us at the front of the church. I had no idea there would be so many mourners; it seems as though there are hundreds. Susanna's wedding was the last time I'd sat in this church, then amongst guests radiating gaiety as they do on such days. Now, wedged uncomfortably between Isabel and Greg, a cold greyness hangs over us. Can that really be the minister? A voluminous figure in a black, swaying tent. Her competent, middle-aged face protrudes from the apex. She seems to vie for centre-stage with my dad in the raised coffin. It is a bleak sight. I feel a shiver go down my back.

Isabel whispers in my ear, "You're doing well lass, you're doing well."

The remark is meant kindly, but isn't gratefully received. I feel irritated by the widespread anxiety over my emotional control. I bet her pockets are stuffed with tissues. God, I hope I don't need to ask for one. I feel so depressed watching my mother gazing pitifully at the coffin, but I am not crying . . .

14

I had always thought Dad would outlive her; the whole structure of her life seemed to depend on him. She'd enjoyed the role of a prominent businessman's wife, meeting his colleagues, discussing office politics, being a martyr to corporate entertainment. Although she often said 'Behind every successful man there is a strong woman', she needed him. His success mattered to her.

Her smart boarding-school in Perthshire suggested she applied to Oxford and to everyone's delight she'd managed to win a place there. She is the type of woman brimming over with confidence, the kind that expects to be the centre of attention the moment she enters a room, good at engaging in conversation with anyone. She likes people to know she has the social edge. It is important that her children behave properly, and right now, their not crying at their father's funeral is her chief concern.

Her anxiety about my strength of mind is reasonable I suppose, and not just because of 'the incident' at my grandfather's funeral. As a child I had always been prone to tears. I look back on them as part and parcel of the asthma that plagued my childhood. Then doctors thought this illness was entirely psychosomatic, the symptoms a cunning device whipped up at will by 'attention-seekers', as the doctors proved transparently obvious in my case. Sent to hospital for a two-week stint, the wheezing completely stopped after three days, and I remained asthma free for the rest of the my stay. This episode confirmed an existing medical theory that asthma was a psychosomatic illness. I was to be ignored and the asthma would stop, the doctors advised my mother. She believed their opinion, accepted their advice, and inflicted their cure with no qualms.

I wasn't regarded as an academic high-flier, but to Mum that did not really matter. The important thing in life was to be strong and successful. She set great store by these virtues - 'personality' as she called it. The frequent asthma attacks (now definitely established as psychosomatic) were a sure sign of a weak personality. You probably imagine it was painful for a proud woman like my mother to acknowledge this reason for my illness. Nature had clearly played a cruel trick on her. However she had a lot of 'personality' and her strength gave her the ability to discuss openly, and occasionally laugh at, her misfortune.

I overheard her once speaking to Granny on the phone. Walking down the stairs, I caught the words.

"She has such a weak personality."

Then silence, while she listened to my grandmother.

"I've told you, we can't do that, she has such a weak personality."

Frozen in my tracks, I tried to stop hearing, powerless to move, hoping she wouldn't know I was there. From the strident tone of her voice, I gathered my grandmother was not altogether agreeing with her, perhaps taking a more sympathetic view of my asthma attacks. The argument continued ping-ponging across the telephone wires.

"We've thought of everything. You've no idea how difficult it is having a daughter with such a weak personality."

It took me a week before I had the courage to mention to her that I had overheard this conversation. I don't know what I expected. Some kindness? Some explanation? But that wasn't her way. It would have been a sign of weakness. With a horrible mocking laugh she said. "Eavesdroppers never hear well of themselves, my girl, remember that."

I couldn't argue with her. The subject was dropped.

I remember the asthma attacks starting, a small tickle in my throat growing and growing, my chest tightening as the irritation spread. I must snap out of it! I must! It was all in my mind. I daren't say anything. It was all attention-seeking anyway. Wasn't it? I would pray. I would curse. I would hope. I would make desperate promises to God. All this and still the attack worsened, the wheezing persisted, rasping and audible as I struggled for breath. And then I wept as at length it burst into a full-blooded attack lasting for days. The effort of forcing air in and out of my aching lungs left me weak and depressed. How had this happened? Hadn't I tried and tried to prevent it, as I was told to. Now the real trouble would start. Wallowing in self-pity and devoid of energy, the coughing fits began. Hoarse and jarring, the pain stabbing at my chest. There were panic attacks when I became desperate. The coughing fits that felt as though they would never stop. I'd crouch forward, shoulders hunched, gasping, anything to make breathing easier. I thought I would die, I wished I would die and then there would be an end to this torment.

In the company of other people my mother made light of it.

"Don't worry, it happens all the time. She just wants attention, she'll get over it."

Then taking me roughly aside by the arm she'd whisper angrily to me.

"Stop it. Pull yourself together at once. You're upsetting everyone and we all know you just want attention."

Repeating in harsher and harsher tones.

"Stop it at once. Do you not hear me? Stop it." When no response was forthcoming, action was taken. Shamefacedly, I was dismissed from the company until I could pull myself together. Curled up in the kitchen chair I would hug myself tightly and shrink into an invisible bubble; that was a refuge from my family.

Mum's friends and family felt immense sympathy for her difficulties with me and helped as much as possible. My benevolent Aunt Ursula would take me off mother's hands for a few days to give her a break, a rest from this problem daughter.

"Ursula has invited you to her house for a few days. Isn't that kind of her?"

Invitation, my foot; it was more of a summons, for there was no option. The two sisters had determined I would go. These dual-purpose visits, giving my mother a rest (which undoubtedly they did) and galvanising me into the mental action required to eradicate my asthma (which they did not) were the worst of ordeals.

Ursula was the youngest of the four sisters, born twelve years after my mother at the start of the war. The midwife had phoned her father, Douglas, to break the good news.

"Ann has given birth to a healthy girl. Isn't that wonderful?"

"Oh," was the only remark he uttered. It was a terrible disappointment, a fourth girl. One way or another this seemed to seal the pattern of her relationship with her parents. Throughout her childhood she was the *bête noire* of the family, a difficult, rebellious child who clashed with anyone in authority and made her sister Barbara's life a misery, even into adulthood. But, despite the twelve year age gap and the aggravation Ursula caused, my mother was closer to her than to either of her other sisters.

Ursula Stone was a woman of substance, due in part to her huge body and moon face that perched precariously between her shoulders. There was actually no visible evidence that she possessed a neck.

The admirable lady made little effort to improve her appearance. The thick glasses she wore dwarfed her small dark eyes, making them appear like little shrunken olives in a sea of flesh. Generally, the clothes she wore were drab. I don't suppose many shops catered for her gigantic proportions. She'd rattle up a little number for special occasions, unfortunately just falling short of decency. Remember, this was the sixties; mini skirts were *de rigeur*. So, at her child's christening, she stood next to her impeccably dressed, Cuban-heeled husband, the chosen Godparent, and the devout Reverend, oblivious to the fact that most of the congregation were on tenterhooks. How long could the luminous orange floral print take the strain of her thighs? My poor grandparents, cringing inwardly with embarrassment, put on a brave face. They had learnt over the years, if not how to accept, at least how to cope with the embarrassment her behaviour brought them.

Despite Ursula's eccentricities she liked to be considered a generous soul, and to prove this to everyone, she'd sacrifice her precious time to give her unfortunate sister a much needed break.

Imprisoned in her shambolic house, she would deal with me. Her sunken olives fixing on me disapprovingly, as though their intensity would help the message permeate my soul, the lecture would begin on her captive audience. She would have a firm word with me. I had heard it all before. She considered she had a duty, a sisterly duty, for family pride had been offended, and it was her right to moralise.

"Can't you see how you're ruining your mother's life?"

"I can't help it," I'd whine.

"Of course you can. Show some backbone and snap out of it. Try making an effort. You know quite well you can put a stop to it if you want to. We all know you just want attention."

I'd heard it all before. Still she would drone on interminably, trying to banish the illness that made my mother's life a torment.

"It's a matter of choice. You can choose to overcome this illness if you want to. You have a free will, you're quite capable of using it."

I'd apologise. I'd try to stop. I'd promise. But even this worthy lady could not eradicate my asthma.

Back in the company of my family she'd air her prejudiced views against me, flaunting the disappointment I was. Listening to her, all I could do was shrink back into the chair, cringing in shame, conscious of the low esteem in which I was held, while my mother sat gratefully appreciating the ostentatious concern and thoughtfulness of her sister. Maybe, in her blustering way, Ursula believed public humiliation could effect a cure.

I sensed my father had some pity for me, even though I could not convince him I had no control over the attacks. He too accepted the advice of the experts and must disregard my behaviour. I suspected at times he may have had doubts, but if my mother had seen any show of kindness from him towards me during an attack, any word or gesture, she would admonish him for playing into my manipulative hands. Her arguments, based on medical opinion, were more persuasive than all my tears, for I had talked to him on occasions, pleading tearfully to try and make him understand.

"I try to stop it Daddy, but it just keeps coming and coming. I can't help it." He'd look at me kindly, unhappy at my lamentations. He would take me on his knee and put his arm round my shoulders comfortingly. He was not an insensitive man and I had the impression he felt at a loss over the wretched situation. But he would not waver from the doctors' diagnosis. Talking to me in a quiet reasonable manner, he too would explain.

"Jenny darling, it's a medically proven fact there is nothing wrong with you. It's all psychosomatic; it's in your head. There is nothing wrong with you. You just want attention. Now pull yourself together and don't upset everyone."

I found his kind matter of fact manner even more distressing than my mother's hard anger. He believed I was a manipulative child wanting attention. I knew this wasn't true, but I had no wish to argue with him. I hadn't the courage to oppose him and risk losing his affection by rebelling. And how could I, a mere child, argue against the medical profession.

What were my parents to do? They did what many parents with difficult children do; they packed me off to a boarding-school for a few years. Initially it was weekly boarding, but as I invariably developed a bout of asthma during the weekends, which tended to continue until about the Wednesday, it was decided I should board full-time. Although I occasionally still suffered from asthma during the school term, while I was away it was no longer a problem for my parents.

However, in the school holidays, I was constantly aware of the difficulties I'd brought to the family. I'd overhear my parents voicing their concerns over money, recognising their feelings of disappointment with me, their despair at my character, the stigma they had to live with. The question was always hanging in the air: 'Where had they gone wrong?'

Even when I was asthma free, the stigma remained along with a powerful feeling that I must show remorse for my 'sin'. I was withdrawn and dejected, guilt-ridden at the responsibility I was made to feel for my weak and exhausted body, for the unease my parents felt for letting a child develop this condition. As a young child, craving their pride and approval, I was painfully aware of the disappointment I was to them. I spent a lot of my time sullen and wallowing in a sea of self-pity, dejected by their frustration. This fed the feeling of rejection, exacerbating the sense of loneliness I felt. I was responsible for this quagmire of hopelessness.

Occasionally I'd decide to make a real effort. I'd study Susanna, the brains and the beauty of the family, my mother's pride and joy. Susanna was her prize bloom, encouraged to grow and branch out; we were all overshadowed by her brilliance. The maternal care and diligence showered on this offspring was transparent to us all but I was the one that resented it most strongly. I'd try to emulate her style, repeat snippets of her conversation, but all to no avail. I failed to capture the vital spark of Susanna that charmed my mother. I had fallen on the wrong side of the fence and would never be admitted to their sanctuary. I was an intruder; any attempt on my part to enter their world would be coppiced down. My mother gained satisfaction from this stunting, crippling exercise, as though, in some way, this treatment was an extension of the doctors' advice. To keep me down, my mother perhaps believed, that was one step better than ignoring me. Criticism would mould my character into something more manageable, more attractive. My response was to unleash my pent-up anger and frustration, vindicating her opinion of me.

It was discovered during my teens that my asthma was due to a cocktail of allergies. Grass, cats, dogs, horses, pollen and house dust were all identified as causes. The physical relief at being given an inhaler that produced a miracle cure at the first hint of an asthma attack cannot be described. However, the pattern of my relationship with my mother was set. Habits had formed and I did not know how to shake them off. She made a few half-hearted forays in an attempt to break down the barriers between us, but we never connected. The resentment and bitterness I felt were too deeply ingrained. Mistrusting any unusual amiability, I believed it to be part of some greater trick she was indulging in to fool me. I refused to respond to unfamiliar affection. Eventually, in exasperation, she'd give up.

"You can stew in your own juice," she would snap out irritably. "What's wrong with you? I try my best with you and this is how you behave."

Or she would try a different tack.

"Have you ever thought what you'll do when your father and I are dead?"

"Bury you," was always on the tip of my tongue, but it was a rhetorical question.

Of my friends, she would sing their praises, telling me of their parents' pride, implying her shame at my failure. It's easy to say I read too much into things, as my father told me when I complained to him, and who knows, perhaps he was right. However, I think my assumption was correct, for I can clearly remember my mother explaining to Fiona her crude psychology.

"The best way to encourage children is to put them down, compare them unfavourably with someone else and they will try and prove you wrong."

This homespun philosophy did nothing to encourage me. Overhearing it, the rebel in me decided I would prove her wrong. Again she would snap at me. "Why can't you be like other children? What did I do to deserve a child like you?"

By some strange masochistic streak I believe this was what I wanted to hear, proof that she didn't like me. This reinforced inferiority confirmed in my mind that these were her true feelings. I would never be acceptable in her eyes, so why bother? The systems had been up and running for too many years. The idea that I was a difficult child was deeply rooted and, by making no effort to rid her of this notion, I somehow felt reassured. Was it that I didn't have the courage to change things or was I just too lazy to make the effort? I would lie on my bed and cry, feeding my persecution complex with self-pity, my head turned to the wall, wishing my mother would comfort me, put an arm round me, tell me she loved me. But the gestures and words never came.

Now, as I struggle to look after one normal child, I shudder at the thought of raising six children, born within eleven years. Even with domestic help, she must have been in a flat spin much of the time.

Chapter 3

Murray Alexander, a friend from work giving the eulogy, knew little of Gus's private life, for he had kept this quite separate from his business dealings. However, Murray must have known my father well, for he captured his spirit perfectly, recalling his dependable, quiet confidence, his skill at deflecting problems with humour and his thoughtful and commanding personality. Having lived down south for many years I had never heard of Murray until today, although he appeared to know all the other members of my family. It was a fitting choice; Murray was first and foremost a business colleague whose friendship had been cemented on the golf course. After all, my father had lived for his work.

Gus had spent most of his working life in the road haulage business, building up one company, Charterswell, only to see it taken over by a large London-based conglomerate, then starting from scratch again to have the same thing happen a second time. The same conglomerate bought both companies for the same reason; the financial backers wanted to cash in on their investments. Such is the way of business.

He loved the rough and tumble of the road haulage business, meeting its challenges and dealing with the various problems, employing and supervising staff, selling the services and setting up contracts, utilising the lorries in the most efficient way, or 'operation research', to those in the know (a very interesting mathematical challenge, I was informed).

Often he was away from home. Every third or fourth week he would spend on a whistle-stop tour inspecting the chain of depots throughout the length and breadth of the country. Then there were the fundraising trips to London to tout his wares round the merchant banks, trying to raise another million pounds as the business continued to expand. He dreaded these visits, although, ironically, it was probably what he was most suited to, moving with ease in the world of the city slickers, having been designed for this set, fortunate enough to have the same blueprint, able to decode the social signs and understand the messages. For it's not everyone who's been privileged enough to have the same education as the movers and shakers of the financial world-corporate lawyers, merchant bankers, investment analysts and-can easily socialise with them on an equal footing. There was a network, he said. This sounded modern and egalitarian, though it depended on pulling strings, providing one was fortunate enough to have the old contacts from the right school, or the right university. I suppose this was the old school tie swinging into action and he could benefit from these contacts; they were a useful commodity in touting for finance.

In the eyes of these city gents, however, he was an outsider, not a professional man, basically 'trade', a road-haulier from Glasgow. He was confident enough to take this on the chin. Dealing with mechanics and lorry drivers on a regular basis, he had few airs and graces. This was the role he'd carved for himself and this was where he felt comfortable, in the company of the Transhire workforce. There was a jocular side to his nature, which revelled in the earthy humour and common sense of these Glaswegians, although he was also an outsider in their presence, conscious of his position as their employer and of their social differences. After all, his father was an Edinburgh doctor and he was an Oxford man. It was understandable that with this background my father was self-assured and confident. It must have been a social juggling act for him, maintaining friendly relations with the work-force but, at the same time, having to deal with tricky situations, such as firing a senior accountant for giving what Gus referred to as a 'horizontal promotion to an obliging young secretary'. I remember him telling us how, at one Christmas dance, he'd had to break up a drunken fight between two drivers in the men's lavatory, a skill that he'd perhaps learnt on the rugby pitch. One never knows when such skills may come in useful.

Greg had been baffled to learn that Catholics and Protestants worked side by side at Transhire. His father had been a loftsman, a highly skilled worker in the hierarchy of the Clydeside shipbuilders. The sectarian tensions in red Clydeside forbade the employment of Catholics in the shipyards. Catholics worked in the construction industry and supported Celtic football club. Greg wanted to know how the open hostilities between the different religions, palpable in the heart of Glasgow and which surfaced so readily on Saturday afternoons, were suppressed in the Transhire workshop. My father answered him in mock seriousness, "That is one problem we don't have with the staff. At work they are united in their hatred of the management."

Gus drove himself hard. He enjoyed the work and he enjoyed the rewards that being the managing director of a successful company bestowed on him. It gave him great satisfaction until, unexpectedly, the company was sold from under his feet.

He'd phoned Greg on the day Transhire was sold.

"I've never heard your dad sound so depressed," Greg told me afterwards. "Clearly he's reeling from the shock."

"He's on a year's contract though; they can't get rid of him immediately." I pointed out. "And won't he make a lot of money out of the shares he owns and the share option scheme?"

"I suppose that will sugar the pill, but that's not the point. Where, at his age, is he going to get another position like the one he's got now, or should I say had? It's a bitter blow for him."

He did benefit financially and apparently it was an open secret that he had intended to establish another road-haulage company with a group he had gathered around him at Transhire, although this was the first I'd heard of it. As he stood in the pulpit Murray Alexander admitted his involvement in setting up this new enterprise and pondered over the difficulties of how the venture would progress now my father was no longer there to spearhead it.

The service dragged on tediously with a chill in the air. Weak rays of winter sun pierced shafts of light through the stained glass windows. Eventually, the four pallbearers struggled to place the coffin on their shoulders. My two brothers at the front, Rory, tall with a red head and a thick red beard, giving him the appearance of roguish good looks, clever, amusing and debonair; for years there had been speculation as to who would be the lucky girl to hook him. What a catch that would be! There was hardly a ball in Scotland he wasn't invited to. A dance in Aberdeenshire, and he'd combine it with a weekend's stalking. An event in Inverness and he'd spend a couple of days fishing in the Spey. In return, his grand friends would drop in on their way south, with their loud tweed jackets, their loud bossy ladies, their intelligent, adorable dogs and their precious guns for a day or two's shooting. Hardly a year went by that he didn't go skiing with some of his more athletic friends, Chamonix being their chosen resort. There were broken hearts and rumours, how he'd partner one girl to a dance and come away with a different one, how he'd drop a girl as soon as he'd seduced her, even dated a friend's fiancée. A few skeletons in his cupboard appeared to enhance his reputation as an eligible bachelor and, until his mid-thirties, he graced many a social function, not only for his natural attributes, which made him a popular guest, but also for those signs of future wealth. For the word '*primogeniture*' lay there like a fine film just below the surface, unsaid, but the echoes rang out loudly. Torlochan, what a fine inheritance for anyone. Rory, what a swell to have at any dinner party! How could he fail to be in demand? He'd managed the farm for more than ten years, with a lifestyle and assurance that declared his success and the confident swaggering bonhomie that proclaimed his intention, not merely to run the farm, but also to own it. He and Henry, the second youngest of Gus's six children, linked arms below the heavy coffin, the closest the brothers would have been for many years.

Henry, aware he had none of Rory's inherent wit or charm, recognised that he, by virtue of his birth, had drawn the short straw in the inheritance stakes. A divide that on the surface he endured with a good-natured indifference, appearing to accept his lot, not as the embittered younger son, as so many younger sons in his position do, nor with fortitude or stoicism, but with good grace. He was kind and generous and friendly, a well-meaning plodder who had worshipped our father and, to my mind, seemed much more likeable. I felt well disposed towards him; furthermore, I felt pity for his predicament.

The brothers' lives followed different paths. Henry's social life revolved around the local rugby club. He was their social secretary, which seemed to involve a lot of helping-out behind the bar, pulling pints and chatting with the punters. He played scrum half for their first team, as a result of which he developed a cauliflower ear, which he concealed below his long locks of hair until he went bald; somehow, things never went quite his way.

Gus had originally hoped Rory would manage the farm as he did, as a sideline, and, after first leaving school, Rory worked for a large timber firm in Glasgow as an apprentice manager; a job he stuck for less than a year, before deciding to attend agricultural college and pursue a career as a full-time farmer. (I think it was a case, of jumping before he was pushed.) Henry also wanted to follow a career in farming and my parents assumed this would be the case as the farm was reasonably large with a choice of farm workers' cottages. However, Rory had a vested interest in creating bad feeling between the two of them. So long as he played his cards properly and made out to our parents that Henry was the one behaving unreasonably, he would be the sole farmer, thereby boosting his chance of inheriting the lion's share of Torlochan for himself.

In Henry there was no duplicity, so when Rory's campaign to discredit him began after he left school and started working on the farm, he was ill-prepared for the assault. I only heard Henry's side of the story, but I have no reason to disbelieve what he told me. Rory instructed him to fertilise a certain field, and then tore strips off him in front of my parents for fertilising the wrong one. At lambing time he was left with difficult sheep to lamb, and when the lambs died he was to blame. A fence he'd supposedly checked proved to be inadequate and the cows escaped on to the road. When agricultural advisers came to the farm he was excluded from the meetings. Rory took him to the market a couple of times and made him look a fool in front of his friends. Henry refused to go again.

"A farmer who didn't want to go to market. Most peculiar," Rory jeered.

My heart went out to Henry. It was an ill-matched duel. Henry, unable to compete with Rory's jibes and taunts, derived some comfort from Arnold's tacit support, but, early on, Rory had Jane lining up as his second. Elizabeth and Fay had also rallied behind Rory. Susanna, I felt, shared some of my sympathy for Henry, but never being one to go against the flow, she joined their ranks. Henry was deeply hurt, his normally sunny disposition changed to one of irritability, interspersed with periods of bitter silences. Rory's plan had proved more successful than he could have dreamt. I tried to talk to my father of the gross injustice, but I was too late. Henry's behaviour had already condemned him. Besides, as my father informed me, the six months Henry had worked on the farm proved financially to be the worst of the farm's history. Those few words I said to my father got back to Rory. Without meaning to I probably made things worse for Henry. He had been complaining to me, a virtual outsider. Dissention in the ranks, they couldn't be having that. What were they to do with him? They decided to pack him off to New Zealand for a year, where distant cousins of my mother's ran a sheep farm. Maybe a year apart from the family and Henry would return more mature and reasonable, breaking down the animosity he felt towards Rory. It didn't work, so Gus found him a position at Transhire.

Behind them was Jack, my brother-in-law. He was not troubled by the problems of Rory and Henry. The only son of well-heeled parents, in his mid-twenties he'd taken his first steps to fly the nest and found work in the south of England. His father promptly wooed him back to Scotland with a gift of a large farm in Perthshire. I remember Rory telling me, long before the farm was bought, that Elizabeth, our sister, who had been courting Jack for many years, would be mad not to marry him, as he had already inherited a considerable personal fortune and would in time inherit yet more of his family's ample wealth. Elizabeth had proved not to be mad and they settled down to enjoy a life Greg and I could only dream of. Nor was Arnold Parrot, the fourth pallbearer, plagued by the brothers' problems. Now in his fifties, living in a tied cottage, his wage was above the level that entitled him to receive income benefit, but not much above. He was a perky, jokey man, happily married to Isabel. If he had complaints I didn't hear them. He came to my parents' sitting room every New Year for a glass of whisky to celebrate the occasion. If this was an ordeal it did not appear so, as he sat comfortably on the sofa and entertained them with his uninhibited chatter. This was his twenty seventh year working on the farm.

As the four strong, upright men raised the coffin onto their burly shoulders they clasped their arms underneath in unison. The men focused their sad eyes on the wooden doors at the end of the church. The effort of bearing the full weight of the laden coffin showed on their strained faces, as they proceeded in their deliberate, measured pace. On the grim, slow-moving journey down the aisle, the eyes of the mourners were on their every step. As they passed the pews, people cautiously moved into the aisles, hampering our way out. They shook our hands and murmured their condolences as we stood waiting for our turn to leave.

The coffin progressed slowly down the aisle and out into the November day. By the time I was out of the church the coffin was in the hearse and the men relieved of their burden. There was a sea of people milling around and talking in subdued voices, more shaking of hands and arranging to meet at the farmhouse after the burial. Some were leaving immediately to return to work, some were drifting up the road to their houses in the village. The village street was crammed with cars assembled in a long line, stretching to the top of the hill. Yellow lines did not exist. People rarely stopped here, where there were only a couple of small shops, a sub-post office and a pub. Drivers would hardly notice this place as they drove through.

There were forces at work marshalling the family into the hired cars, with more mourners in cars trailing up the street. My mother and Ba sat quietly in the front car with Fay, Greg and me. Greg averted his eyes with false nonchalance as he examined the other side of the street, as though fascinated by the kerb design. He appeared to ignore all that was going on, avoiding all eye contact. He knew that Jane would consider his tearful performance in the church as a cultural betrayal. Andy Rose opened the car door.

"Are you ready to go now, Mrs MacKenzie?" he enquired with the same courteous deference he would have employed if consulting her over the type of finish she had chosen for a new kitchen work-surface, and she, in the same vein, answered in a business-like tone.

"Yes Andy, whenever it's convenient for you." How could she be so strong? This must be the worst journey of her life and she was so much in control, so calm.

Andy stood in front of the hearse and started to walk out of the village with the cortege behind him. It seemed incongruous to see Andy in his new guise as undertaker. As the joiner he appeared slow, ponderous, every word carefully articulated in his strong sing-song Glasgow accent. His cloth cap didn't fit quite straight on his head and his gaze would rest on you, guileless, friendly and unassuming. I used to wonder if he might be slightly simple, but then he would explain why a dining-room door was hung in such a way, so the diners would have a couple of seconds warning of the company entering the room,

"Psychologically it's best to hang the door this way," he would explain slowly.

Now, when I saw him as the undertaker, in literally a different hat, I found it difficult not to smile. He was dressed in a dark suit, claw-hammer jacket and black top hat. His voice was full of sincere sympathy, concern, and reverence for the occasion, aware of the sobriety of the event and his part in it. I could only see him as the joiner acting the part with a surprising ability. He walked ahead of the hearse as it glided sedately out of the village, with that slow deliberation that was the hallmark of Andy, confident that he was doing the correct thing. As I watched him I felt a giggle coming up from inside me. Perhaps it was relief that the funeral was over without tears on my part; perhaps it was the effect of the valium tablet or just the strange sight of Andy, the man I knew as the carpenter, elevated to this new role and performing with such unimaginable tact, courtesy and decorum, the part of the undertaker. The man with the scruffy dungarees, the pencil lodged permanently behind his ear as if implanted, and the lopsided, self-conscious grin, was transformed into a dignified figure. Yet I couldn't take him seriously, as this tragic occasion demanded, and as hard as I tried to suppress my amusement, anything to stop these giggles coming, it was all to no avail. The force was too strong; they bubbled out to the surface and infected Fay. We sat in the back of the car and giggled as we watched him.

Apart from the clothes and the grin nothing else had changed, yet in my arrogance I had never rated this man as more than a slow-thinking tradesman. Was he going to walk the one and a half miles to the graveyard with almost one hundred cars behind him? Did he enjoy this moment of power, having control over so many mourners? There would not be many funerals in the village to rival this large and impressive gathering. However, I think it was more a ritual he used as a mark of respect for all funerals. As soon as the hearse was out of the village he climbed into the passenger seat beside the driver and the cortege duly arrived at the graveyard for Andy to render his final act for my father.

There were tears at the graveyard, but not mine.

Chapter 4

Only ten days previously my parents had moved two hundred yards further up the farm road from the main farmhouse into a state-of-the-art Nordic kit house, built on the site of the old gamekeeper's cottage. This downsized and upgraded in one stroke. Possibly it was this dual action that was too taxing for my dad's heart. This was to be their retirement home, a three-bedroomed house with spectacular views in all directions. Like my five brothers and sisters, I owned 8% of the farm. The previous year my father had asked us all to sign legal papers gifting the spot where the old cottage once stood. This included a small 'wood', now consisting of a mass of undergrowth, fallen birches, a large majestic horse chestnut tree and a few straggling beeches trying to survive. Thrown in for good measure was a six-acre field that sloped down to a stream that marked the boundary of the farm. As the 8% share of the farm had been a gift from my parents several years earlier, it seemed odd, somehow churlish, to then sign papers to gift the land back to them, but my father wanted all the procedures carried out properly. This would ensure there would be no misunderstandings now, or in the future

Many of the mourners returned to Torlochan, where the caterers had been busy while we were at the church. The Scots, like the Irish, know how to enjoy a wake. The sitting room quickly filled up with neighbours and old family friends, relatives and business colleagues of my father's, seizing a glass on their way in.

Ursula decamped with her brood and their assorted accents. As a staunch nationalist she'd lost a lot of street-cred because of her Anglicised private-school accent. However, she had no intention of burdening her children with this affliction. Her left-wing principles meant her children would go to the local school, have local friends, local accents, local interests. They would be 'locals'. Reality set in when her eldest son left school at sixteen, bought a woolly hat and started working on a local building site. This was not the kind of 'local' she'd had in mind. The other siblings were hurriedly packed off to boarding-schools, local boarding-schools of course. As a result her children's accents spanned the spectrum from broad Hawick to refined Edinburgh.

My mother took Greg by the elbow, "I think I should introduce you to John Anderson," was all I heard her say as she steered Greg in the direction of my father's old school-friend and lawyer.

Having no wish to talk to any of the Stones, I let myself be cornered by Ba. She married my widower grandfather when she was fifty, and was the archetypal Edinburgh schoolmarm, orthodox and churchgoing, working tirelessly for worthy causes. She was riddled with the traditional attitudes rife amongst the prudent Calvinistic ladies of her type, with their sensible lace-up shoes and practical sheepskin jackets that lasted for donkeys' years. Ba had no truck whatsoever with any modern, new-fangled theory. Horrified when one of her fellow mistresses married the Polish immigrant who ran the garage, she always referred to him as 'Johnny the Pole'.

"Although," she affirmed, "he must have some good in him; he gives money to the Conservative party."

She too was steering clear of the Stones; unfortunately she was heading in my direction.

"You must be nice to your mother," she instructed me in her schoolmarmish way, "she must be in a state of shock."

"I'm in a state of shock as well," I replied.

She didn't like being answered back. "It's a lot worse, losing a husband than a father. I should know, so you be nice to her."

I saw Angela, Elizabeth's sister-in-law, smiling at me. Saved, I grabbed a glass and made a beeline in her direction. I liked her better than her brother, she was less of a snob, and although our circles barely touched, we 'clicked' as she put it. While I'd left school to nurse, she'd followed another route for the less academic, a finishing school in Switzerland. Two years later she married a distant cousin and moved to his family estate near Oban. Once we'd been pony club friends. We still were friends of a sort, Christmas card friends, connected by a family tie, even though we had little in common. We chatted for some time until she was called away by her mother.

I recognised Mrs MacPhearson who was wandering around, dipping into the nibbles and looking a bit lost. I summoned my courage and went over to talk to her.

"Hello Mrs MacPhearson, how are you? Are you still living at Gartain?" I enquired politely.

"Yes, yes." Her voice had lost all its authority. This was the woman I had been terrified of as a child. Now, with her wide eyes swimming round the room from under her hat, resting on no one and nothing, and smiling aimlessly, she appeared child-like herself. She wore a beautiful powder-blue coat suspended limply from the shoulders and a wonderful broad-rimmed matching hat, with her fine halo of grey curly hair peeping out from underneath. Clearly she'd lost none of her dress sense. She had been an attractive woman when young, tall with red wavy hair hanging down over her broad shoulders. She was opinionated and fierce, widowed when young. A strong woman, people said, and I understood what they meant when I saw her pushing a cow onto a float, one shoulder wedged between the animal's rear legs. Now I realise what they meant for it is no easy task for a woman to raise four children on her own and run a farm. She'd had a hard life.

"Which of your children is running the farm?" I persisted in my effort to make conversation.

"Yes, yes," she repeated, and with a jolt I realised just how much she had changed.

Henry came over to rescue me. He must have seen the shock on my face as I discovered the state of Mrs MacPhearson's mind. She had just arrived, and now she wandered off to sit on a sofa and wait, like someone who had spent too long at a party and now only wanted to go home.

"She's been like that for several years. Priscilla is very good with her, takes her out a lot, but she lives in a nursing home; she's got some form of dementia."

George Cramer came over to talk to us. He had probably been my father's closest colleague at Transhire as well as being deputy managing director of the company, and was being groomed as his heir. He had been reared in the road haulage business. His father and uncle, both lorry mechanics, ran a garage on the outskirts of Leeds. His hands moved in all directions at once as he talked. I imagined the agile body slipping below the underbelly of a lorry, his hands jutting out in the same dexterous fashion as he tested the machine for faults. In his evolution to the vertical pose his hands had failed to progress and still darted all over the place.

Transhire's principal interest in buying the family garage was because of its location, and George had come as part of the package. As Gus was a manager, so George was a salesman to the ends of his fast-moving fingertips, fast-talking, fast-thinking, and in his BMW fast-driving. Rory, with a snide reference to George's wife, many years his senior, referred to him as the over-wound toy boy, and I could see exactly what he meant, even his eyelids fluttered too quickly as he quivered with all his pent up energy and excessive enthusiasm. He seemed very uncomfortable now, as though his body wasn't taking the orders, his will was transmitting to slow down, and the reactions were not co-ordinating properly. George was to have been managing director in the new company with Gus as chairman. Gus was a good foil for the excessive energy that exuded from George's vibrant body, mirroring his dynamic personality. Gus had been quiet, dependable, commanding, with the innate confidence and polish stemming from his public school background. Together they'd made a winning team.

He spoke to me for a few minutes, but neither of us was sure what to say. George still worked at Transhire, but his days were numbered, as were those of many of the staff who'd worked with my father. It's probable his mind was plagued by more pressing issues than making small talk. His future with the embryo company he'd planned with my father as the figurehead must now be in doubt. The worry was that the financial backers would pull out now Gus was no longer there to oversee the enterprise.

I'd met George once before when he'd been in London with my father. Being in his company then had been easy as he chatted readily. He did listen politely when I spoke, but I could see he was happiest holding court, reciting amusing anecdotes about the guide dogs he and his wife bred, his local golf club and stories about his business life. He, like my father, loved the road haulage business. Every day was different, it was so interesting and varied and there were always new developments, he enthused.

I couldn't think of any thing more stressful, though for someone whose adrenaline appeared to be pumping away relentlessly late into the night the perspective would be different.

"Each to his own," I'd commented wryly.

He'd laughed and with a complete lack of political correctness answered, "This isn't a woman's business."

Devoid of the bonhomie I'd seen in him then, he wandered off to commiserate with some ex-employees who had already been made redundant and were job-hunting from the dole queue. It had been a sudden, hostile take-over and MBX had been ruthless to the unsuspecting staff, who were still reeling from the shock. Most of the office staff from Transhire were at the house, talking in groups and paying their respects to the family, before drifting back to Glasgow.

Greg, having been introduced by Jane to John, stood close to the older man, by the French windows. Amongst the general mixing and moving, the darting out of hands at passing trays of drinks and nibbles and the jovial chatter and gossiping, the two men locked in earnest discussion looked an incongruous pair, out of tune with the general mood of the occasion. There was much nodding and shaking of their respective heads, grimacing and looks of perplexity as the conversation progressed. Every now and then the talk would stop as Greg threw his head up and looked with narrowed eyes at the back of the room as though working out some complicated mathematical formula, and John leaning against the wall, gazed at the floor. Anyone looking at them would assume they were established business colleagues from Transhire locked in urgent discussions.

As the afternoon wore on and the guests left, my mother and I found ourselves chatting companionably on the sofa. My mother told me she'd arranged a meeting for Saturday morning to discuss my father's will. There were four executors: Jane, Rory, Greg and John. John had recently retired and his legal successor Peter Wright would also be present along with the farm accountant, Jimmy Geddes.

Chapter 5

Greg and I spent the following day admiring the new house, listening to Jane's plans, tidying up and preparing for the meeting the next day. Henry, aided by Greg, moved the furniture, stacked the books on the shelves, hung pictures under Jane's instruction and gradually the sitting room looked as though it had been transported up from Torlochen, lock, stock and barrel.

Henry was living at Burnside since being made redundant from Transhire. Gus had been kind enough to find him employment at Transhire and his position had been safe as long as my father managed the company; unfortunately, he had been a casualty in the first round of redundancies after the take-over and was now selling insurance on a commission-only basis; he would never again have the advantage he'd had at Transhire. He would have liked to work on the farm, but Rory's lack of brotherly concern for Henry had ruled out that possibility. He was deeply troubled by my father's death, shocked, as I was, and having difficulties coming to terms with it.

I had offered to cut a loose cover for the kitchen sofa. This was how I made my living, making soft furnishings, but mainly loose covers. Phillipa called in while I was busy with pins in my mouth. She took one look at the fabric and instantly voiced her concern to my mother.

"I think she's using the fabric inside out." I bristled inwardly with indignation, I wouldn't have gone into her kitchen to check that she was using the correct ingredients for a soufflé, especially if it was nothing to do with me. As they discussed the minutia of the fabric, I cut the loose cover.

That evening the rest of the family had been invited to Rory and Phillipa's for a meal. It had been impossible to find a babysitter for Alex, we were told, so Greg and I would have to stay in at the new house on our own. Exhausted after the events of the last two days, we felt relieved to collapse in front of the television with sandwiches.

"It looks as though there may be problems with the farm," Greg told me that evening. I'd heard this before; there were always problems with the farm and they were always sorted out in the end. I was more concerned about the next few days; Jane had asked me to stay on at Burnside to help her for the week following the funeral; it was the last thing I wanted to do but I could hardly say no to such a request, especially as I'd played no part in the funeral arrangements.

Early on Saturday morning Rory arrived at Burnside looking, every bit the gentleman farmer, with files of farm accounts and relevant papers pressed tightly under his arm. John Anderson and Peter Wright drove up together. John, tall, relaxed, confident, was probably not too delighted at having his weekend interrupted. Peter Wright was a small, dark, bespectacled, almost Woody Allenesque figure, hovering nervously and anxiously, a conscientious man who could be relied on to proceed properly. Even John seemed amazed at the quantity of documents he produced from the back of the car

"I didn't want to forget anything," he explained apologetically as we watched in amazement at the number of journeys he had to make from the car to the house.

"Obviously not," John commented dryly.

I felt sorry for Peter. He looked as though he was walking into an enemy camp fearful that he might be thrown to the lions. It must be nerve-racking to have one of the senior partners present to say nothing of all the relatives sitting in at this onerous task. Jimmy Geddes was the last to arrive with even more files.

Rory suggested that Alex and I visit Torlochan. He probably wanted us out of the way. A woman and a two-year-old were not wanted around at this time. So Alex and I put on boots and sauntered down the untarmacked road towards the old farmhouse and the adjoining outbuildings. As a child I must have walked and ridden down this road hundreds of times yet I'd never noticed until today the fascinating configuration of lines and contours of the old farmhouse and outbuildings, the stable, the hayshed, the silo and the tractor shed, the corners and irregular angles of the architecture developed haphazardly over the years, for agricultural buildings need no planning permission.

As our family had expanded and because assorted relatives and friends were forever visiting, my parents had decided the house needed extending. Building a porch between the farmhouse and the barns, they were able to convert farm buildings into two extra bedrooms, a bathroom and a farm office, thereby blending all the buildings into one large, strange, straggling, amorphous shape. The whole complex stood out vivid and bright, bleached in a coat of whitewash, stamped boldly against the muted colours of late autumn like a modern sculpture with a rag-rolled backdrop.

Those eighteenth century builders knew a thing or two. Something we were going to find out very soon. Separating the farmhouse from the farm buildings meant separating the residential quarters from the rats. For Elizabeth and me, living in the converted barn meant living with rats scrambling about overhead. Sporadically the rat catcher would come and lay down rat poison, eliminating our unwanted visitors, and for a few weeks we'd have no overhead disturbances until the next generation of rats moved in. It was surprising how quickly we became used to the rats and their nocturnal activities and learnt to turn a deaf ear.

As we ambled slowly towards the house, Alex struggled to pull his little feet out of the muddy patches. Occasionally his foot would come out of the boot altogether and standing on one foot he'd grab onto me for stability, frightened his foot would land in the mud. I had to bend down and pull the top of his boot; it was like pulling suction pads out of a drain. The foot was replaced in the boot and we continued on our ponderous way.

Eventually we arrived at the farmhouse and knocked loudly at the kitchen door. I wasn't surprised Phillipa didn't hear us, so, uninvited we took our jackets and dirty boots off in the porch and entered the room I knew so well. I suppose it was the movement of the door that alerted her to our arrival, because she looked around startled. Standing there feeling foolish and out of place in my socks, I smiled at her and said hello. I can't say she looked the least pleased to see us. Nevertheless she had the grace to offer me a coffee. Alex and I watched in awkward silence as she boiled the kettle and searched in a cupboard for biscuits. She gesticulated to me as she placed the coffee on the table; I was to sit down at the kitchen table.

"I need a coffee too," she said by way of opening the conversation. "Rory and I have hardly been able to sleep since your father died. We're going to have major problems paying the inheritance tax."

"I've had difficulty sleeping as well."

"But you don't have any financial problems?" Her remark struck me as somehow inappropriate.

"No," I answered with incredulity, "it's because of the emotional shock."

While I sat drinking my coffee she started to talk to me of her aborted plans.

"We wanted to do work on the house, nothing structural, just modernise the house a bit. A new fireplace in the sitting room, replace the kitchen units. I find it impossible to cook on the Aga. It's a monstrosity. I really need a new oven."

Perhaps I had been a bit unfair to the girl, I thought, assuming she was trying to take my mind off my father, and I had to agree with her. The kitchen could do with a facelift. It had never been, shall we say, a state-of-the-art affair. It was a farm kitchen, part of the house and an extension of the farm, the one room in the house which the farm workers were allowed to enter if they needed to heat milk or take a drug out of the fridge for a sick cow. The plain wooden cupboards stretching the length of the room, built by Andy Rose's father almost thirty years ago, may have stood the test of time, but even then they had been merely utilitarian and now they simply looked beyond the pale. The Aga, a large, bulbous breathing organism, the heart of the room, took up most of the back wall, functioning 24 hours a day. I cannot remember a time when the Aga was not burning. It heated the water and kept the kitchen and dining room warm. In the early spring, the premature lambs suffering from hypothermia were placed on a tin tray, which was first covered with a cotton cloth to cushion the lamb and then placed in the coolest of the four ovens, and here with the door left open, the immature lamb was left to recover. Clothes were for ever hanging over the rail at the front of the Aga, rapidly drying, and if an express service was needed the hob lids were put down and clothes neatly folded across the top of them, but care had to be taken in these hurried drying cases as there was always the risk of singeing the garment. When the wind blew in a certain direction, the fumes it belched out filled the kitchen with smoke.

On the coldest winter days or nights the men, frozen to the bone, hobbled into the house. Their limbs would be stiff with cold as they made a beeline for the Aga. Holding their arms up over it, fingers outstretched, the toes of their boots pushed against its base, too cold for any supple movement. Gradually the feeling returned, and they would rub their hands together, bending their knees and rotating their ankles. Like a wooden doll that was coming alive they would exhale a deep breath. "That bloody cow, I thought she was never going to calf."

I sat and looked nostalgically at the 'monstrosity' as Phillipa carried on.

"I don't even know if we'll be able go on living here, or if Rory will still be farming. We've only just moved into this house, and now we might have to think about moving out. It's terrible; I had no idea Gus was so badly advised. I was going to buy a new car, the one I have at the moment is pretty rusty, now Rory says I'll have to make do. We wanted to start a family soon, that's got to be put on hold as well. On top of all this we're having a big housewarming party on New Year's Eve, the invitations are all out and most people have accepted."

I looked at her in surprise.

"I don't know what we are going to do," she grumbled.

If she wanted my sympathy, tough, she wasn't getting it. I felt I deserved sympathy more than her, hadn't I just lost my father? Disgruntled, we sat looking at each other across the kitchen table, each disappointed the other was not offering the sympathy we felt we deserved. We would never be friends, Phillipa and I.

"You don't seem to understand how awful the situation is for us with inheritance tax," she said determined to up the stakes in the compassion contest. "We are going to get a tax bill of £150,000 just for inheriting our share of the land."

I felt the nerves twitch in the back of my neck. It was in response to 'our share of the land', it seemed a shade too presumptuous, when I was still unaware of the contents of the will, that she was laying claim to her share. Listening to her, I suddenly felt annoyed, being in no mood for this cold-hearted conversation. Unfortunate circumstances had wrong-footed her, and overnight her ordered existence had changed, throwing her plans into disarray, dragging her into an abyss of self-pity. Impoverished farmer's wife was not the role she had envisaged.

"There are problems with the partnership as well," she continued. The partnership comprised what I suppose could be called the disposables, the machinery and the livestock. The plan was that the company made money by renting the land to the partnership. Why organise the finances in such a convoluted fashion, you ask? Historically this was the best way for tax purposes and, presumably, if the partnership went bust the farmer still owned the land.

I recalled the Christmas when my father had told us we were each getting 8% of the farm. So between the six of us we owned 48% of the company.

"Not enough to organise a mutiny to overrule me," he pointed out. "Also," he went on, "if for any reason in the future the farm is sold you will each get 8% of its value. If Rory or Henry want to farm they could buy you out." The fair-mindedness of my father I had taken for granted. As for the possession of these shares, they lay dormant, playing no part in my life. I took no interest in the farm and no dividend was ever paid.

"The partnership belonged to my parents, won't it just pass directly to my mother?"

"We own 10%. It was given to us by your parents as a wedding present. There is some big tax advantage that applies to farmers if they gift 10% of a farming partnership to an offspring when he marries." She didn't sound the least bit grateful. Plainly this had not been one of the chosen items on her wedding list.

"Rory's so worried about the inheritance tax, he's hardly been able to sleep for the last few nights."

Sitting, robot-like, my mind consumed and exhausted by grief, I listened mechanically to her words. She was way ahead of me, contemplating the material consequences of my father's death. My brain felt as though it had not functioned since the tragic event.

I'm not so hard-hearted that I didn't feel a twinge of pity for her plight. A week ago she must have thought how fortunate she was, living in this charming farmhouse. Gus's untimely death twisted all this into a bad dream. However she seemed completely insensitive to my grief. All her talk was of inheritance taxes, sitting tenants, her aborted plans, the gloomy state of their finances, the threat to their lifestyle and the unlikely prospect of them remaining on the farm. I'd had enough of this financial gloom and despair so, as a distracting technique, I asked Phillipa to show me how they'd furnished the rest of the house. Not that I was particularly interested, but anything was better than the present conversation. We wandered through to the dining room. The large un-curtained window was highlighted, in stark contrast, by a polished, Regency-style dining table, perfectly set for six people. The cleaned silver cutlery shone next to the crystal glasses. Two glasses for each neatly arranged place setting.

Another dinner party, I thought. *You're busy. My family yesterday and friends tonight.*

The tour ended in the sitting room and we sat on the chairs as Alex romped on the floor with her spaniel, oblivious to the discussion going on over his head, for it was in both possible senses, in fact a lot of it went over my head. I sat subdued, stung into silence by this defiance of decency, as Phillipa with a dogged determination continued to drone on. It was as though I wasn't there. So things weren't going exactly her way. Expectation has a lot to answer for. Golly, what was I doing at her age? I shared a flat in North London with four other girls; not only a flat, I shared a room.

The meeting was expected to stop at midday, so I left the house as soon as I could, bristling with indignation. Phillipa had to finish decorating a trifle for our lunch, and then follow us up to Burnside shortly.

My ears were still full of Phillipa's depressing words as I returned to Burnside, and, as expected, the seriousness and gravity of the meeting had stamped an air of gloom on everyone there. Rory's features were rigidly composed as he said farewell to the lawyers, both of whom were understandably eager to go home. Jane was still unusually calm, with none of her customary pertness showing, as for the first time in her life she was in control. Up to now Gus, as a natural organiser, had always been in the driving seat, taking an amazing interest in every detail, able to grapple with all the facts. He took pleasure in managing the financial side of the farm, with what Jane regarded as a ludicrous degree of caution in all business transactions. He'd kept a firm hold of the reins, curbing her immoderation, a fact she had resented. She felt he didn't trust her and this caused a niggling irritation and tension between them.

She sat now and listened to Rory, as he reluctantly asked Greg to explain in layman's language what exactly had been said at the morning's meeting. Normally he would not have asked Greg about a thing to do with the farm. What would a 'townie' know about it? Now Rory had little option but to discuss the most sensitive financial issues with him.

On first acquaintance they'd made an attempt at friendship, but they weren't compatible. Rory's confident public school charms and impeccable social etiquette masked a selfish personality, with no kindness for those less privileged than himself and scant regard for the self-made man.

He liked to meet up in the evenings and weekends with other young bloods of his ilk, the well-heeled beef farmers, affluent sheep farmers and the barley barons. And in their socialising they'd complain about the poor prices they received at the market, the lack of support from the government, whining about their lot while at the same the time promoting their high-minded ideals and charismatic personalities. They regarded themselves as the misunderstood guardians of the countryside, cleverly defying the powers that be that had marshalled against them. From this high-minded position they had no time for the 'the plebs that sponged off the state', and 'the no-hopers from the council estates'.

Greg's background was completely at variance with these jolly good chaps; his state education, steeped in the Presbyterian tradition, had not prepared him for this aspect of society. Greg was capable of making up his own mind and was not impressed by Rory and his friends. They in their turn were fairly contemptuous of Greg and his 'sound investments'.

"Where's the smart money going this month?" they'd ask him mockingly.

Giving financial advice is a thankless task, Greg had told me; you get the blame if it goes wrong and no credit if you get it right.

"I wouldn't like to say," he answered them truthfully.

I suppose he realised that if by some miracle he landed in the same financial league as these men, he would always be recognised as a nouveau riche upstart. They had been poured directly from their mother's breast into the appropriate mould where they had congealed into the desirable set. What they valued most, their social status, Greg could never have.

What he valued most, his education, meant nothing to them. He had been fortunate enough to pass the eleven-plus and had learnt early how privileged he was to be given a Grammar School education, something his own father had never had.

'From those to whom much has been given, much shall be expected', had been a favourite and often repeated expression from his headmaster. This is what he was taught and this is what he believed.

So there we have it, different products of different systems. One that accepted that the only hope lay in the application of hard work coupled with a degree of intelligence and integrity. The other dependent on inheritances and handouts, cherishing the subtle nuances and social niceties of his set.

In no time at all the pretence of friendship was destroyed. They were not destined to be more than brothers-in-law. On the rare occasions when they met, Greg, to his credit, refused to respond in the same vein as Rory but instead turned a blind eye to his ill-mannered behaviour with polite indifference.

Greg was not impressed by Rory and his friends so he did not care for their good opinion, but I was rankled that they held us in such low esteem.

"You have to recognise we'll never be in the same league as your family," Greg tried to reason with me. "It would be foolish of me to pretend that I was in the same class, you knew that when you married me. There aren't many people who don't have to struggle to make a living, hold down a job and pay the bills and I'm not one of them." All this was true but it didn't make me feel any better. It was not what I wanted to hear.

Gus was the one member of my family who genuinely liked Greg. He shared his interests and enjoyed his light-hearted banter. Sadly this bond deepened the rift between Greg and Rory. The previous year, when Gus had asked Greg to be an executor of his will, he was stunned as it was so unexpected.

"I would be happy to," he blurted out, flattered at being asked, embarrassed at what he thought was probably the wrong phrase to use in such circumstances, and adding more tactfully: "Of course, that would be no problem." Greg had felt it would be indelicate to say anymore and Gus had offered no explanation. The matter was never raised again.

Until today Greg had no idea how the financial side of things had been arranged, but this morning he had found out in detail. As a pension consultant, he was on his home territory and his competence and expertise in these matters was not lost on Rory. I sensed the discomfort as he reluctantly asked Greg for clarification of obscure phrases used by the lawyers, 'the residue of the fee', 'dead spart', 'reversionary interest', 'life tenancy' and other such incomprehensible terms.

Greg's explanation was given in the manner he knew best, as though to a client who not stupid, was understandably not as well versed in these matters as he was, and in this manner Rory was able to maintain his air of condescension.

"Come on, let's go through to the sitting room and talk to Fi and Jimmy," Greg said, keen to shake off the gloom of the last two hours. I shuddered inwardly, embarrassed on Rory's behalf.

We wandered through to the more relaxed atmosphere of the sitting room where Fiona and Jimmy were sitting comfortably in front of a fire. Fiona, 'a great talker', as my mother always described her, was large, jolly and ample-bosomed. She appeared to be the most content of the four sisters. Jimmy, a quiet man with a shy, self-deprecating sense of humour, lounged back comfortably in my father's old chair as the others followed me through. It wasn't long before Phillipa arrived, her hair now swept back in a clip, wearing tight trousers and a smart jumper.

She had brushed off the blues and it appeared as though all the complaints, despair and misery of an hour ago had been shed and she had found a hidden strength. My company had been useful while she wanted sympathy. She turned to my mother and enquired politely how she was, an unspoken reference to how she'd coped with the meeting. Jane looked grateful and gave her a regal smile of approval.

"All right thank you Phillipa," was all she said on the subject. "What a wonderful trifle you've made. I'll put it in the fridge."

Rory passed her a glass of white wine. I saw his eyes meet hers, there was no reassuring smile, no confident gestures, just a glance, a silent message conveyed as he took a deep breath and shrugged his shoulders a fraction. Words were unnecessary, but I could read the body language loud and clear; financial havoc lay ahead.

By now it was evening, the lunch guests had become high tea guests, largely due to Jimmy's near obsession with gardening which had compelled him into lengthy discussions over matters horticultural. He dispensed advice on garden design and planting, the shrubs which grew best in this type of soil, how large to make the rockery, which plants to grow on the north side of the garden, and whether to plant a hedge or have a boundary fence or attempt to integrate the wood into the garden and which trees should be cut down.

"Not the horse chestnut," I remonstrated, "I love it; it's the most beautiful tree. The place would not be the same without it."

Jimmy judged it to be to too large and overpowering.

"It should go," he said, and my mother appeared to agree.

Only after he and Fiona had left for Edinburgh did the subject of my father's will surface again. It was early evening, as the three of us sat watching the remnants of the fire that had burnt all afternoon, its embers flickering slowly. Jane started in earnest to discuss the problems of the will with Greg. She told us how the farm hardly ever made any money.

"Gus propped up the farm financially for years you know. It hardly ever makes a profit." I listened with surprise. I had no idea Rory was not making a go of the farm. He'd always given me the impression of a prosperous farmer with a flourishing business and money in the bank. If this was the case, his lack of success had not affected his lifestyle in any way.

"I won't be able to support Rory financially the way Gus did. There are a lot of things he can do to cut back the expenses. Fertiliser for the fields is the biggest expense and there is no need to use as much as he does. He wanted to buy a new tractor next year, but the present one should last a good few years if he maintains it carefully. Gary, Mrs MacLeod's son, from the village helps in the holidays. He's interested in farming and we've always paid him, but we can manage without him; I hope he'll understand. As for Arnold, I don't think we'll be able to give him a pay rise next year. There is the shooting. Rory can always let that out and it will bring in a good income. I know he enjoys inviting his friends to shooting parties and many of the wives shoot as well. Phillipa was hoping to take it up, but she'll have to put it on hold for a couple of years. They both desperately need a holiday, but I think they'll have to give skiing a miss this year."

I felt an outburst coming on: *can't you see what a lazy, spoilt, good for nothing he is? It's about time he started doing something for himself, try to make his own way in life, rather than depending on other people all the time.* Instead I contented myself by sourly remarking, "He'll have to pull in his horns."

"Of course, I'll do what I can," she continued obstinately, ignoring my comment. "If Rory does any work for me, fencing, digging, planting or whatever, he will have to give me a proper invoice and I'll pay him a commercial rate." She might not be able to prop up the farm the way Gus had, but she'd pull out all the stops in order to help him.

Rory was far from stupid; I could not understand how he could be so unsuccessful. Farmers were cushioned from a lot of the stresses of reality by the various grants and subsidies that were doled out, prices were guaranteed, and agricultural advisers visited regularly to tell them of their entitlements, discuss new farming methods and help with any relevant problems. It was unlikely he would make a fortune farming, but I could not understand why he should make a loss.

"We could reduce the rent paid by the partnership to the company," Jane continued, trying to think of other ways to turn around farm finances.

I'd seen these fretful signs before as her conversation yo-yoed from positive and practical to the doubts and worries that kept surfacing time and again. She was as distressed and anxious over the dire business as Phillipa, only her approach was more pragmatic. She had been here many times, lurching in and out of financial crises; this had been the rhythm of her life, stressful times interspersed with periods of comfort. Educating six children privately had taken its toll even though Gus had always been well paid. There were times when juggling the family finances had been an ordeal, but somehow they had always managed to make ends meet. The crises passed somehow, in the shape of a cheque for a farming subsidy, a generous bonus from Transhire, or the grant for last year's sheep.

Greg was here to help and she listened to his comments as he gave her his considered opinion. She appreciated his grasp of the technicalities of taxation and legislation, yet for all his expertise he was still an unknown quantity. She had never really trusted him, why should she now? Gus had listened to and relied on Greg, believing he gave the best advice and that fact should have reassured her, but still there was a nagging doubt. Was it that the problems, as Phillipa had said, were graver than before, more insuperable? Perhaps that explained the worries that kept resurfacing.

"You could develop some of the barns into cottages or convert the courtyard and sell it. You have all the facilities there already, running water, electricity, tarmacked road. I'm sure you could get a good price for it," Greg suggested.

"It's an idea, but even doing that I don't think we would raise half the money to pay the inheritance tax. Also, Rory and I don't like the idea. Once the buildings are in someone else's hands, you have no say over what they do with the property. There'll be strangers walking around the place, driving their cars up and down the farm road. They could have dogs that'll worry the sheep or leave gates open and let the cows out. I don't want to encourage people I don't know to come here."

"I know Jimmy has valued the farm very conservatively to try and keep the inheritance tax down, but I don't know if the Inland Revenue will accept it. These people usually want to make their own valuation," Greg said, "we'll just have to wait and see what they come up with."

"You've weathered storms before." I tried to reassure her, feeling that Greg's response would only add to her anxiety.

"Not on this scale, and your father's salary is no longer here to bail us out. I have a good pension, but it's not enough to support the farm."

It wasn't until we fell into bed that night that Greg was able to confirm Phillipa had been correct in every detail relating to the will.

"Your mum is well provided for. She has a lump sum from the pension fund of two hundred thousand pounds, the new house with the field and the wood, and an index-linked pension of twenty-five thousand pounds a year. That's more than the average wage and with no mortgage to pay and her children grown up; she should be all right financially. And as Phillipa has informed you, she owns the major share of the partnership and a substantial part of the company. She may have had to scrimp and save when you were young and they first bought the farm, but your mother is a rich widow now."

Greg left for Reading first thing on Monday morning, abandoning Alex and me with my mother. I knew I wasn't there for comfort. I was there to help, and the days were taken up with the grim practicalities of bereavement. Gus's old clothes needed to be disposed of, dental appointments had to be cancelled, bank cards closed down and funeral expenses sorted out.

There was constant activity; frequently I acted as waitress to the stream of visitors calling to pay their respects. People kept arriving with newly baked cakes, scones, fresh eggs or flowers, some just on their own to offer their condolences; pressed to stay for a tea or coffee, they readily accepted. Many of them were widows welcoming Jane with open arms to their burgeoning ranks.

"Have you ever thought of curling, Jane? It's a wonderful sport, we practise every Tuesday afternoon at the ice rink. You should come along with me sometime."

"I was wondering if you would like to make up a foursome with our bridge group. We've been at a bit of a loose end since Molly moved back to Edinburgh to be near her daughter."

Relieving them of their offerings, I took on the part of the housekeeper, scurrying off to the kitchen to do my bit. Arranging the large wooden tray with the best bone china cups and saucers and placing the teapot on the tray, I would quickly wipe my hands, and hope this was the kind of gentility the lady visitors would appreciate. Carefully I'd place the tray on the coffee table and proceed to pour the tea cautiously into the cups, hand them to the ladies, offer them a cake and then, hovering attentively, as a dutiful daughter might do, I would wait for a sign that the company was happy with the service before disappearing back to the kitchen for a mug of coffee. Sometimes the conversations would appear to be very confidential; my mother and the visitor would stop talking when I entered the room with the tray. My mother would give a brief nod, indicating she would do the honours with the teapot, the good lady focusing her eyes on my mother, indicating that the conversation was strictly *à deux* as I beat a hasty retreat to the haven of the kitchen. I was there to be of help, not a comfort.

Even the postman rang the doorbell on his morning delivery and sputtered out quickly in his awkwardness, "I'm sorry to hear about Mr MacKenzie's death."

"Yes David, it's very sad," Jane admitted, taking the letters, unable to look him in the eye.

Phillipa visited us a couple of times, bringing a stroganoff on one occasion for our evening meal. She talked mainly to my mother, treating me with a casual indifference, for which I was relieved. She talked to Jane about the hens she was keeping, asking Jane's advice about the best feedstuff to give them before they became broody, how many chicks she could expect in the spring from each hen? She thought she might go on a lambing course at the nearest agricultural college so she could help Rory and Arnold in the spring when they were at their busiest with the new calves and lambs. Phillipa had the sense to appear interested in the farm and was obsequious enough to consult my mother as an authority about agricultural matters, well aware of the passionate interest she had in the farm. The shared interest and flattery were having the desired effect, fuelling my mother's feelings for Phillipa. The garden was another common interest as my mother told her of her plans for the mud bath that she currently looked out onto. She thought she would have a rockery at the back of the house and mainly shrubs at the front. A friend of Phillipa's grew unusual herbs near Glasgow, would Jane like her to take some cuttings for her garden? Yes Jane would be delighted, how kind of Phillipa. She agreed with Jimmy, the chestnut tree should go, it was too large and dominated the garden. Had Jane thought of leaving a few feet of tree trunk standing, incorporating it somehow into the garden design? What a brilliant idea, that's what she would do. Phillipa was so creative.

I could just see it, this noble giant felled and reduced to a perch for a garden gnome.

There were phone calls, lots of phone calls. Susanna and Fay seemed to call daily, Susanna sometimes twice a day and this appeared to be the norm. My mother and I frequently spent many months with no contact and when I did speak to her it was usually because my father had phoned me for some reason. I had never imagined she spoke so regularly to her other offspring. I imagined they might speak once or even twice a week, but not this frequently. There were phone calls from lawyers wanting clarification on details, wanting phone numbers of people to clarify more details, wanting details of bank accounts and building societies. There were phone calls from Transhire arranging to collect the company car, with what seemed like indecent haste. Calls asking about files Gus had taken home, wanting to know where Jane's pension payments were to be made. There were phone calls from friends who had left the area and only just heard the sad news, acquaintances who had been away for a couple of weeks and not been informed, old university chums who he hadn't seen for years, and then there were the letters. Every day brought an another bunch of letters. I had no idea there would be so much to do. By the time the evening came

I was exhausted. We'd have our supper, and then I'd put Alex in his cot and collapse into bed myself.

As the week rolled on I saw my mother's energy draining and I felt her attitude change, as though the grief and exhaustion mellowed her feelings towards me. At the evening meal we'd sit down and talk and with the early darkness of the northern winters the mood changed. I say we talked; generally she talked and I listened, as the practicalities of bereavement were overtaken by a brooding anxiety for the future of Rory and Phillipa. Her conversation fluctuated between the threatening financial catastrophe hanging over them and melancholy concerns for their domestic plans.

"I can see how envious Phillipa is of you having a child." I'd never put her coolness towards me down to envy. Did my mother genuinely attribute her behaviour towards me as jealousy? "She's desperate to start a family of her own but it's impossible at the moment, it would just put an unbearable strain on Rory," she continued.

Rory also was a changed person. The change was as great in him as the death of a parent could produce. Apart from the grief that such a loss causes, he had the added worry of managing and maintaining the farm without the encouragement, assistance and financial safety net Gus had provided. However his greatest anxiety was the problem of paying the inheritance tax. He was unable to hide the effect the strain was having on him, even during the week I stayed at Burnside there was a notable change in him. His face wore a haunted look as though he hadn't slept for days, the bags under his eyes darkened, sinking them further into his face, and the weight rolled off his body as the week wore on. For the first time in his life he knew what it was to be under pressure. Striving and grappling with the complexities of the present situation was taking its toll on his disposition.

He had been catapulted into a situation which in the natural course of events would arise, but I suppose he believed Gus would live until his nineties, as his father had done, and not die unexpectedly in his early sixties, leaving Rory ill-prepared to cope with a financial crisis.

In the midst of all Rory's despair, Jane took pride in the change in his character.

"He gets more like your father every day," she announced with satisfaction one morning, as he drove past the kitchen window on the tractor.

It did appear he was ageing rapidly. He was quieter, more sombre and thoughtful than before, which was hardly surprising considering his present problems. Jane had always leaned heavily on Gus and now I suppose she was hoping she could transfer her dependency to Rory. Hopefully the circumstances would improve his character, yet I could see no growing resemblance to my father.

Henry was Jane's real worry. She could accept that he was not very bright, but what she could not understand was that his public school manners and bonhomie would not provide the opportunities she expected for him. He had been through the public school system; the system would look after him wouldn't it? It didn't matter if he was less able than most, he had the contacts, the pals from the system. It had worked for her generation why shouldn't it work for her son's? Surely they wouldn't see a public school boy in a pickle? Jane was determined he would get a job befitting his background. The trouble was, there were all these other types rotting the system. They may be clever but you couldn't trust them, they hadn't been to the right schools and they didn't know how the system worked. It was all so confusing, this new fangled culture, this topsy-turvy social order, refusing to conform to her outworn social standards.

If Jane lowered her sights for Henry, he too might lower his expectations and find employment that he could cope with and enjoy. He eagerly took Alex off my hands and they played for hours. The childish amusement that Alex showed Henry buoyed him up, and for a while the problems of his present existence evaporated.

They held hands and ran down the road to watch Arnold mend the tractor and returned muddy and exhausted, exhilarated by the afternoon's entertainment. It was touching to see Henry talking gently to Alex as they played on the sitting room floor with trains and lorries, remnants of Henry's own childhood.

Looking at him, I thought employment in a children's home would suit him, but I couldn't even hint at such a thing. Jane would be offended on Henry's behalf. In her eyes I was the one who didn't understand the ways of the world and to propose such a course for Henry would confirm my lack of judgement. He needed insight, intelligence, intuition and an incisive mind to be engaged in the world she planned for him, not what he offered, which was a kind nature and pleasant manners. Why couldn't my mother realise this?

One day for a break I decided I would stroll up to the Axle coffee shop with Alex. Here Isabel gave us a cheerful welcome.

"Would Madam care for a biscuit?" she joked as she surreptitiously slipped a biscuit onto my saucer, and then being mid-week in November and the Axle being quiet, Isabel joined me at the table for a chat, while Alex disappeared to the corner with the toys and left us in peace. Inevitably the conversation turned to a discussion about my father.

"He was always very good to us, your dad. We don't know what will happen to us now. Rory's not a bit like him."

It had never occurred to me that Gus's death would affect Arnold and Isabel. Arnold was like an essential piece of machinery, how could the farm manage without him? Like an office without a computer, it wasn't practical not to have him there. Even more surprising was that Isabel should express her fears to me. She knew enough about our family to be aware of the tense relationship that existed between us. Still I had never before heard her criticise my family, and I was surprised at her taking me into her confidence like this. Although she had always been friendly towards me, she knew on which side her bread was buttered and it was in her interest to remain on good terms with Rory and Phillipa, especially now that Arnold's future seemed precariously dependent on them. I felt slightly uneasy listening to her express her misgivings. Surely this wasn't the done thing, discussing my brother with his employee's wife. I wondered if there was a subtext I couldn't decipher or was she genuinely expressing her nervousness about her future to a sympathetic ear? Was she hoping I would relay her fears to Jane? I didn't ask. I listened, for it was reassuring to know other people had similar feelings about Phillipa. It wasn't only a case of sour grapes on my part; other people outside my family noticed the airs she assumed.

"Arnold doesn't like Phillipa. He thinks she plays on her disability to get her own way. Do you know the night your father died she went off to Makro to buy food for her housewarming party. Can you imagine that Jenny? The night he died!"

Of course I knew nothing of this badly timed shopping trip, but I knew the party was planned for New Year's Eve, six weeks away.

"I thought she'd have the decency to cancel that party, considering the circumstances."

"We've been invited," Isabel said.

"That's more than we have."

"We didn't want to go anyway, but we are certainly not going now. Seven weeks after your father's death she plans to have a housewarming party in his old house that he gave her. It's disgusting. She expects us to treat her like the lady of the manor, swanking around spending money like there's no tomorrow. When I think of how your mum used to scrimp and save and make do. Who does she think she is?"

"Arnold doesn't get well paid, but it's enough to get by on. We both like the cottage and we'd be hard pressed to find another garden as big as the one we have here, but any extras come from the money I make. At least the children are off our hands now and all working, so that's one less worry."

Our conversation was interrupted by a couple of customers dropping in for afternoon tea. Isabel bobbed up to the counter to take their orders. She asked them if it was still raining outside and suggested they try some banana cake.

"It's freshly baked today and tastes delicious," she encouraged them.

The Axle belonged to Jo and Jenny Grey. Jo was a builder and his talents had been put to good use converting the old stone cow shed into a coffee shop. On the main road to the Trossachs they could hardly fail to succeed as the tourists streamed past in the summer months. In the winter, there were regular customers who called in for a light lunch after a game of golf, local ladies wanting to take a friend out for a coffee or families taking Granny out for a special weekend treat. Gus had said a couple of times that the Axle made more money than the farm. Then I had thought he said it tongue-in-cheek, but after hearing Jane's comments on the farm's finances, I now believed it was the truth.

Walking back slowly to Burnside with Alex at my side, I thought of the number of lives affected by my father's death. I, like Phillipa, had only thought of my own distress, but now I recognised that the boundaries of other worlds would be shaken. George Cramer and his colleagues from Transhire would probably see all their plans collapse, and what had Isabel been telling me between the lines, that Rory and Phillipa would soon be down-sizing or that she and Arnold no longer wanted to work on the farm?

Nearing the end of the track to Burnside, I looked up and saw the large chestnut tree standing starkly against the clear sky. This year's leaves had blown down weeks ago. Upright, strong and defiant, it might suddenly at any moment disappear into the ubiquitous grey drizzle, changing the whole scene in minutes, until the autumn winds swept off the gloom, to reveal it once more. Wiping out this landmark on the horizon, a focal point of fun and excitement every year for children when the conkers fell, would be sheer folly. This majestic tree, grown and matured for over a hundred years, could be cruelly destroyed for a few transient specimens purchased from a garden centre. Jimmy had suggested the best thing was to fell the tree, since it would overshadow the garden, and Jane had agreed with him. Once her mind was decided on a course of action there would be no stopping her. However, I'd talk to Mum and try and persuade her to keep it.

That evening my mother raised the thorny subject of the money I would in due course inherit from my father's estate.

"I would like you all to put money from your inheritance into the new business your father was going to start with George Cramer and other colleagues from work. The money you will receive was earmarked for this new enterprise, so I think it is only fair that you invest a good chunk of it in the new business."

I said nothing. It seemed a bit premature, there was no knowing how long it would take to wind up the estate and why should I want to sink the bulk of my inheritance into a company that, from what I could see, was being set up on no more than a wing and a prayer? If my father had lived, it would have been a completely different matter. I had faith in his ability to manage a road haulage company, wasn't it what he had spent the last thirty years doing? As a shareholder in the company, it would have added a new dimension to our conversations.

"How are my shares doing Daddy?"

"Very well, we've just landed a big contract with . . . Corporate Ltd. to supply and maintain four hundred lorries over the next three years."

"What does that mean?"

"What does it mean? It means we're going to buy four hundred more lorries and employ many more mechanics to service and maintain them. Leonard is looking for two more depots . . ."

"No. What does that mean for my shares? Am I going to get a dividend this year?"

"Well I don't think so. We'll have to re-invest the money to purchase the new lorries."

One thing I knew about the road haulage business, it eats up a lot of capital. If my father had been alive, I wouldn't have had the capital to invest. Now I had money coming it could pay off my overdraft, reduce our mortgage, we could have a bit of a flutter on the stock market, but not in a road haulage business, no thank you. There would be no ready market for my shares if I wanted to cash in on my investment. Once George had the use of my money, I would have no say in what he did with it, although I did not for one moment think it likely he would behave fraudulently. He just wouldn't have the power to release the money once it was invested, and the only occasion on which I could monitor my stake would be at the AGM when the annual accounts were issued, and I couldn't imagine that either would give me a great sense of enjoyment. I could think of a hundred different ways to spend my money and a road haulage business was not one of them. The enterprise could jack-knife badly, swing out of control with spiralling costs, and go off the rails with the risk-taking George Cramer in the driver's seat.

"You will in due course inherit a sixth of your grandfather's substantial estate. It's being held for you in perpetuity until Ba dies." I looked at her in surprise at the sudden interest in her mother-in-law's death, only days after seeing her off to Edinburgh. Up until this moment the subject had been taboo, now it seemed it was open season. Was this some mawkish association of ideas or was she trying to convey a message? Your father's will may be a mess and take years to clear up but don't worry; you'll be in the clover when Ba dies. We have to be sensible and consider the long view, look at the overall picture as part of a business plan; the chance of Ba surviving much longer is fairly slim. I felt uneasy; it seemed in bad taste to discuss the practical consequences of her death, as a conversation piece, in such a calculating way. She seemed to sense my scorn at this mercenary interest in Ba's death.

"Ba asked me last night if I would be an executor of her will," she said by means of explanation. "Your father was the executor of her estate along with the lawyer. Obviously she must appoint someone else. I suggested Rory. I think he would be a more sensible choice than me." I remained silent. This was not the point she had been making. She had been referring to the inheritance I would eventually receive, not the executor of the will. Was I expected to enquire what was in it for me? Somehow it didn't seem appropriate.

"Ba also told me she intends to put £20,000 of her own money in the new road haulage company." She said, returning to the original point. Surely George hadn't been touting his wares round a newly bereaved family looking for funding.

"Did George ask Ba to invest in the new company?"

"No, she intended to put the money in when she heard about the project from your father several weeks ago, and she told me yesterday she was still intending to buy shares, only she'll invest them in Henry's name and I've told George I'll provide a further £20,000. I am going to talk to your sisters and suggest they invest a similar amount," my mother continued, interrupting my thoughts. Ba was putting money in, in Henry's name? I could see their angle, sink enough money into the nucleus of the company and buy Henry into the position he would have had if my father were still alive.

"Why don't you use the money to pay the inheritance tax? Do you have to put money into George Cramer's new business?"

"Yes I do. It's what your father intended to do with the money and the road haulage industry has been the goose that laid the golden egg for us. I've got to think of Henry as well." *And,* I thought, *these investments would be a link with her newly past life, for my father's death would sever all ties she'd had with his business life.*

"Does George intend to employ Henry in the new company?"

"I hope he does," she answered, in a tone of indignation. "Your brother knows the people involved in the new company and he is familiar with the road haulage business. I'm not at all happy about what he is doing at the moment."

"From what you are saying they will be running the business on a shoestring," I said. What I didn't say was that if Henry was to be employed in the company it should be on his own merit, not because his family had pumped as much money as they could into it. I could understand that £20,000 would be ample as a goodwill gesture, but not £20,000 from all his immediate relatives.

"Yes, it's a bit of a worry for them, I don't think the institutions will want to invest money now your father's not here."

"With all the money you're investing you could buy Henry a flat in the west end of Glasgow."

"There's not much point buying him a flat in Glasgow if he ends up working in Leeds."

"It would be a good investment, he could always rent it out."

"I like to think of a house as a home to live in, not purely an investment," she said with an edge in her voice. I guessed which way the conversation was going and before any snide references were made to Greg's brother, who made a good living out of renting out flats, I let the matter drop.

Despite our difference of opinion, the week passed surprisingly quickly, and amazingly, by the end of the week, she was like a different person towards me. This spell was cast perhaps in gratitude for my help or the knowledge that, thankfully she could depend on Greg to help her through the confusing financial maze in which she found herself. He had a good grasp of the situation and was glad to be of service. I left the farm on Friday morning on better terms than I had ever known with my mother.

There wasn't yet the easy camaraderie she had with her other children, and I admit it rankled with me that she was grateful for Phillipa's fawning manners, impressed by Susanna's great wealth and connections and amused by Fay's zany ways. These were traits I couldn't admire, but so what?

The old tensions had been cast aside. It was a sad irony that my father's death should have brought about this sea-change in our relationship.

Chapter 6

Perhaps I've painted too black a picture of my childhood. Life was not all gloom. I had what every little girl dreams of, my own pony, Spice. Maybe it's because he's essentially a cerebral urban man that Greg still finds it difficult to understand the relationship between a young girl and her pony.

"All that flesh pounding rhythmically between your legs, of course I can understand the attraction," he once commented salaciously.

I tried to explain it was the freedom to ride for miles and miles. I spent hours of my childhood riding along old railway tracks and across moors. I'd take picnics and spend the day going through glorious countryside. Galloping or walking, whichever the mood took me, it was pure escapism, abandonment, moving in harmony with this beast and all the while I was in control. I spent days of my childhood riding through Loch Ard Forest in this way; how I loved those adventures, never knowing where the tracks would lead. To him it was all pretentious nonsense. I loved caring for my pony, nurturing him, grooming him for hours while he munched from a hay bag.

Spice wasn't the only source of comfort to me. After I left the boarding school, I was sent as a day-girl to a small private school that was just within commuting distance. (I suspect the bus fare was less than the cost of boarding.) To break up the commute, I spent Tuesday nights at my grandparents' house as they lived only a few miles from the school. Here I was fortunate, for I adored my grandmother. She was my friend, my solace, and my soul mate. After supper I'd sit on a stool beside her chair listening as she talked of her strange fragmented life flitting between Africa and Scotland, husband and daughters. As she talked she taught me to sew. Her sewing skills were learnt in Africa from Hilda. I met Hilda once on a trip to Edinburgh with my grandparents. Hunched up, she emerged like some witch from the Underworld, whiskers all over her face, emitting weird guttural noises and calling me Jane as she stroked my face with her grotesque, claw-like hands. She frightened me, the ugly old ghoul. In reality she was a wizened old German widow trying to eke out a living in a basement flat on a meagre pension, but to me as a child she was a hideous specimen of womankind.

It was on the boat out to West Africa that Douglas and Ann met Hilda and Cecil. Cecil, a child of the manse, was following in his father's footsteps. He had taken Holy Orders and had prayed to work as a missionary in China, where his brother-in-law and sister were stationed, but the Church in its wisdom decided West Africa was where his talents would be of greatest benefit. My grandparents were heading to West Africa for a different reason, to make more money. My grandfather was going to work for the Colonial Office in the forestry department. He was a hard-working practical man, determined to take advantage of every possibility and improve his lot.

Cecil felt that his posting to Africa was a punishment for the 'sin' of his marriage to a German. Ann and Hilda were drawn together by default. Hilda, some thirteen years older than her husband, was undoubtedly a social anomaly amongst the young colonial women of middle England, brought up to despise 'The Hun'. Nor did Ann fit into the social scene, partly because of her friendship with Hilda, but not entirely.

Ann was an intelligent, well-educated young woman. She had no desire to conform to the social graces and codes of conduct of the ex-pat wives, finding the phoney gentility of their lifestyle oppressive and boring. The bridge parties were not to her liking and the gin drinking brought back memories of a childhood blighted by her father's heavy drinking habits.

Ann hated being referred to by the Africans as 'Madame'. The surly subservience of the word, forced out in a sullen drawl, with all the connotations of the word coming into play. She told them how she disliked the word, so they called her 'White Man', perhaps because of her unusually short hair. At least she found this name amusing. Somehow, along the way, the name Mrs Douglas evolved. This display of familiarity from the African houseboys was abhorrent to the more established members of the colonial service.

However, the life in Africa fascinated my grandparents. Like all the other colonial families, they had staff to help in the house;

a cook, a houseboy and a dhobi to wash clothes. For some reason all the houseboys were Nigerians, living in houses that were no more than shacks, some distance behind the big house. Despite their meagre accommodation, they were all given a patch of land and here they kept hens. They were small, scrawny, half-starved birds that scraped and pecked at the red soil all day, until dusk, when some primitive instinct drew them to the hen huts for the night. There had been the strange occasion of an eclipse late one morning, and to Ann's mind the most remarkable sight was the spectacle of the confused hens falling over each other in their rush to enter the huts at the unexpected nightfall. Ann enjoyed the evenings most. She and Douglas would walk down to the beach and swim in the warm sea, the place alive with the sound of insects and lizards.

The cook bought 'chop' every day. There was never any fresh milk so powdered milk was used. Exotic vegetables, never even heard of in Scotland, were served. Occasionally, the cook would return from market with a live hen which he tied, by its leg, to a tree until just before it was time to cook the poor wretch.

Shopping was very limited. Sometimes in the early evening the Haussa man would call. He was a Muslim from Nigeria dressed all in white, selling household goods. If the men needed clothes they had to rely on the efforts of the inmates of the local prison. Women had to bring their own clothes from Europe, unless, like Hilda and Ann, they made their own.

Douglas must have felt he had come a long way. His own father had been a chauffeur for many years until the First World War. Then the lady of the house assembled the male staff in the hall, instructed them on their patriotic duty, gave each man a guinea and assured them the war would be over by Christmas, and that their positions would be held open for them. All but one returned, and sadly that one was not my great grandfather, who perished in the trenches. Douglas now boasted his own chauffeur, servants in the house and an office full of African staff at his disposal, reflecting the power and authority of his position as a Colonial Advisor to the Government.

I don't think his own chauffeur could have been a conscientious fellow, for I remember one story he told me with great mirth. On one occasion he had been on a trip deep into the jungle with his driver. They had taken a motorbike as the track was not suitable for a car and on the return journey he had somehow managed to fall off the back of the bike. The driver did not stop and at first Douglas thought it was a joke, but he soon realised this wasn't the case. He continued walking along the track for several hours until the driver eventually returned full of apologies. He hadn't realised that he had lost his passenger until he arrived home. What amazed me about the story was that my grandfather survived. Wasn't he frightened that he would be attacked and killed, possibly eaten alive by cannibals? My questions were far more amusing to him than his story was to me. There was never any danger to Europeans in Ghana. White women could walk the streets at night, safe in the knowledge they would not be attacked. What about snakes? A snake could have eaten him! No, snakes only attacked if you disturbed them. The only reason Africans killed the snakes was because they swallowed their chickens whole!

Ann went with him to visit the gold mines at Dungah, 3,300 feet down in a lift where she thought she'd reached Hell and would die in the airless heat. She met an Ashanti chief, who gave her a stool, which I have to this day. More often she travelled to the mission house at Aburi up in the mountains and stayed with Cecil and Hilda, and it was here that Hilda taught her to sew, a skill which she passed on to me.

In Aburi, Cecil's job as a minister was to help in the administration of the Presbyterian schools. All the schools in Ghana at that time were Church schools: Church of England, Methodist, Presbyterian or Catholic. There was one church school in each area, so the locals were introduced to different brands of religion depending on the area they lived in. The ministers of all denominations, Catholic fathers included, although poorly paid, were held in high esteem by African and British alike. In Africa Hilda was happy. Here she was the wife of a valued member of the community, impoverished by the standards of most Europeans, yet revered.

Cecil's family had taken Hilda to their heart. She had travelled to Scotland after the war to care for her dying brother.

He had been captured in 1915 and spent the next three years in a P.O.W. camp, where he met and became friends with Cecil. Her brother had survived the war, quite content to improve his English and play chess in that godforsaken place until the November of 1918, when the doctors diagnosed cancer. He was to live less than two months. In those two months Hilda fell in love with Cecil and stayed on in Scotland after her brother's death. Her direct, straightforward manner appealed to his Presbyterian principles, but not everyone in Britain took such a kind view of a German. Memories of lost brothers, fathers, cousins, uncles and fiancés were fresh in the minds of many and the idea of Christian forgiveness was a long way from most thoughts.

Hilda and her family had also known suffering. She felt guilt about the death she'd escaped, the only survivor of the staff from the school where she'd taught. Two brothers dead and her father's tailoring business destroyed during the war. The only time she spoke to Ann of her wartime ordeal was when the anonymous letter appeared. The anonymity disturbed her, the not knowing; but the real distress lay in the intense hatred of the words, the vindictiveness and the hostility. Why should she bear the guilt about a war she never wanted, would there be no end to it?

Africa, the white man's grave, took Cecil before his thirty-fifth birthday, a few months before the end of his second spell in Aburi. Hilda, not only heartbroken at the loss of her husband, was in despair over her own future. She wanted to return to Scotland, to be close to Cecil's family. She could not stay with his parents indefinitely. She must find work. But what? A woman of her age, and a German to boot. What was she to do?

It was about this time that my grandmother discovered she was expecting her first child. In general, European women did not have their babies in Africa, as the risks were too great. So, several months into her pregnancy, Ann left Douglas and returned to Edinburgh, where my mother was born. As was the accepted custom, Ann went back to Africa when Jane was nine months old, leaving her daughter in the capable hands of Hilda. Ann knew Hilda would care for her daughter well, giving her all the attention she could and treating her as though she was her own. It was to be almost two years before Ann saw Jane again.

Cared for by Hilda, showered with all her Christian love and devotion, Jane had, Granny told me, all the qualities of an adorable child, fun loving, friendly and blessed with the good looks inherited from her father's side. Hilda had kept her promise and looked after Jane as her own, truly her own. Yes, the child spoke German. Ann was horrified. Why had no one told her in their letters? Douglas's family must have seen her almost daily, living so close. Why, oh why hadn't they informed her? The child understood English well enough and spoke a smattering of the language, but the songs she sang were German and her childish chatter as she played with her toys was German, at night in her sleep, the words escaping from her subconscious were German. Her first language was German.

Unsurprisingly perhaps, Ann was expecting her second child. It was to be another girl, Fiona. Hilda, now in her fifties, was needed in Germany to care for her dying mother. This time Ann would remain in Edinburgh until the girls could both speak English. There might be problems with her daughters, but a language barrier was not going to be one of them.

We children were brought up on the story of how, after Granny returned to Ghana two years later, Jane cried for a week, causing a squint to develop in one eye. She wore glasses for several years after this and she and the few other girls who wore glasses at the school she attended started the Goggle Club, exclusively for wearers of spectacles. When Alex developed a squint at five and the optician asked about our family history, I recounted the melancholy story of my mother's squint. She thought it probably a coincidence, the crying and the squint.

I am no psychologist, but I feel here I must give you a thumbnail sketch of my mother's family history. Her actions, and I should also add lack of actions, dictated by a combination of snobbery and weakness, are at the heart of the story I am about to divulge. To give you a true idea of her worth, her social and academic accomplishments, I must go back two generations.

All four of her grandparents hailed from the mining area east of Edinburgh. Ann's parents had married when in their teens as had Douglas's mother, his father having reached the ripe old age of twenty-three when he tied the knot. The fact that Ann's mother was as keen for her daughter to have a university education and a profession as her son was unusual for the time, although, given the family circumstances, not surprising. Ann's father had fled the family home for Australia when she was fourteen, compelling her mother to abruptly find a job as a shop assistant in a shoe shop. She hated the work; it was exhausting, frustrating and badly paid, but having no skills, she had little choice. Douglas's mother, as a widow, was also forced to raise children on her own in an impoverished state. Thanks to the Carnegie trust, both Ann and Douglas were able to attend Edinburgh University, where they first met.

Jane's early years, as I've already described, were spent in Edinburgh. She saw little of her parents, but lived with her sister, under the care of Hilda. Nearby were her grandmother, an aunt, uncle and cousins, and her childhood was on the whole a happy one. At eight, she started at a smart boarding school in Perthshire. As Douglas worked for the Colonial Service he could send his daughters to good public schools at the taxpayer's expense, and hopefully they, like their practical, determined parents, who made the most of every possibility, would also be sensible enough to take advantage of a good education. To give them their due they did. Jane gained a place at Oxford, Fiona went to R.A.D.A. Ursula went to Edinburgh. Barbara, the apple of her parents' eye, surpassed them all. Pretty, witty, musical and phenomenally clever, she won a prestigious scholarship to Cambridge. Even as an adult, mother complained how she and Fiona had to help with the housework, while Barbara practised the piano. One night disaster struck. A keen campanologist, she climbed the church tower at 3a.m. and started ringing the bells. During the war this had been a warning that the Germans had invaded, but the war was over. Amidst widespread confusion she was carted off to the local psychiatric hospital and never took up her place at Cambridge.

As a young woman Jane had been beautiful and even now was strikingly attractive. She'd never lost her figure and kept the poise and mannerisms of one much admired by the opposite sex, girlish and flirtatious, yet appreciated for her intelligence. She had thick dark hair with large hazel eyes that drew one like a magnet. Her voice was deep and giggly and switched playfully from one mood to another. She had a great fund of confidence for her intelligence and beauty, and felt her station in life entitled her to be treated with great admiration, but as I have already mentioned she set considerable store by her own toughness. Like her sister Ursula, she had a way of assuming that what she said was of paramount importance. A lack of confidence was never a problem; somehow the humility gene had completely bypassed these two ladies.

It seemed to me she'd never matured past being a student. Her flirtatious manner had stood her in good stead at Oxford, where at that time only one student in nine was a girl, and of this minority a great many were blue stockings, with little interest in boys, she had told me. My mother, not being of this bent, had a whale of a time. Many of the male students, like my father, had fought in the war, and were no longer 'wet behind the ears' as she put it. "Those were the best years of my life, I could go out with a different man every night if I wished."

Understandably, with her formative years spent in this environment, she had a high opinion of her own appeal and, crowned with the superiority of her Oxford education, she was acutely aware of her importance in society. Her ambition, she had informed my grandmother while she was still at university, was to be engaged before she finished her degree, hopefully to a doctor. *What a shame*, my grandmother had thought, *all that education and all she wants to do is get married.*

She might not have achieved either of her objectives, but she arrived – socially. The Mackenzies were the epitome of genteel Edinburgh respectability, the family littered with lawyers, engineers and doctors, with hardly a whiff of scandal. There was the story of a reverend uncle who'd been obliged to move to Canada after a parishioner had caught him swearing in the street for some reason. All in all Jane had done pretty well for herself; she hadn't succeeded in marrying a doctor, but she'd managed to hook the next best thing, a doctor's son, a doctor's only child no less, and within a year of leaving university. It seemed as though things came pretty easily to her.

She felt affronted that I had not married well. Greg refused to let the social difference trouble him, and I don't think it bothered my father. They chatted in an unselfconscious manner as members of any family would do, about anything from the Scottish football team's poor performance last week, to new government regulations regarding whatever and the effect they would have. It irked Jane that Greg appeared unconscious of the social divide. For Greg the only difference was that, through a quirk of Jane's father's employment, she had been educated privately at the tax payer's expense.

"I don't know why your mother is so snooty," Greg would occasionally comment. "Let's face it, her father was little more than a jumped up-lumberjack, and if he hadn't worked for the Colonial office in Ghana she would probably have attended an ordinary school like me. Whereas my father was a skilled worker in one of the most responsible trades of the Clydeside. Hundreds of jobs were dependent on what he did. His career was every bit as important as your grandfather's."

Sadly, that was not how Jane saw it and, for all Greg's analytical and logical mind, he was unable to appreciate the social distinction that segregated him from Jane, and she, aware of the laws of her social class, submitted to his indifference with a thinly veiled condescension. I remember on one occasion when visiting the farm, Greg and I discovered that Susanna was dating a young Indian doctor.

"You know about the importance of a generous dowry to a man from a good Indian family," Greg chaffed my father, "and you know what can happen if the dowry's not sufficient," he chortled, enjoying the financial insinuation to his own position.

Gus smiled wryly, amused at this joke at his expense, literally, and enjoying the friendly banter.

This was a style of humour to which Jane did not take kindly. Greg was implying they were tight with money. She smiled in a way that indicated she was not amused at his remarks. Indignation was setting in; soon there would be an eruption. I gave Greg a kick. But I digress.

Back in Henley, Greg was catapulted into the business of executor. Screeds of documents arrived from banks, detailing balances of accounts, entries passed through accounts after my father's death, standing orders and direct debits cancelled, building society accounts closed; pension queries, enquiries on the valuation of the farm, questions on income tax. The whole affair was mind-boggling.

Letters were followed up by phone calls, with Greg returning at lunchtime to discuss serious matters with Peter Wright. Discussions were held in a grave reverential manner, for money is a grave business and the correct degree of reverence must be applied, especially when dealing with a practitioner of the law as he explains the difficulties and complications of the will, far too complicated for anyone but a lawyer to understand. And all the time the costs were mounting.

"Surely there must be some way round it?" Greg remarked. "It may be complicated, but is it necessary to be so complicated?"

"You don't seem to understand. This isn't a case of just closing down a couple of building society accounts. A complicated will like this, involving the Inland Revenue, could take several years to wind up," the lawyer replied, exasperation creeping into his voice.

Greg wasn't to be put off the scent by a lawyer throwing jargon at him. If you can't get over a problem, you search for a way round it; you dig underneath until you unearth it, and root it out. Somehow, you find a way. There is more than one way to skin a rabbit. He bought books and studied the information. He thought he had it. He wasn't sure. He remembered that one of our neighbours in Islington had been a trust lawyer. He'd ask him, double-check. Yes, Roger confirmed it, he specialised in drawing up 'Deeds of Arrangements'. Greg had it now; it was so simple, there must be a catch. He must check one more time, just to make sure, to be absolutely positive. Perhaps Peter Wright knew something he didn't know. He'd ask him.

"A Deed of Arrangement. That is a possibility, so long as all the beneficiaries and trustees agree to it."

"Is there any reason why they shouldn't?"

"I can't think of any."

A Deed of Arrangement is a legal means of reducing inheritance tax. There is no inheritance tax between spouses. If my father had left the bulk of his estate, less £128,000, to my mother, there would have been no inheritance tax. As it was the taxman demanded 40% of anything over £128,000 not inherited by my mother. A 'Deed of Arrangement' could be executed by the beneficiaries and trustees of an estate all agreeing to give the inheritances (less £128,000) to the spouse. This way the tax man would be sidestepped. There would be no tax liability.

After a few months, Jane would be free to distribute the shares according to my father's wishes. So long as she survived for seven years after the donation, no inheritance tax would be liable.

"What do you think?" Greg asked.

"What is there to think about? Tell Rory and my mother about it now."

"Once your mother has the money, the law would regard it as hers, and then at some later date she would redistribute the money according to your father's wishes."

"Yes I understand that."

That evening Greg phoned Rory.

"Your brother's not stupid; he asks all the right questions," Greg remarked after the call.

"Such as?" I asked.

"Is a 'Deed of Arrangement' legally binding? Why didn't the lawyers suggest it?"

"What did you say to that?"

"I told him it was legally binding."

"No, not that bit, the bit about the lawyers not suggesting it."

"I didn't say anything; he can work that out himself. Rory's going to speak to Peter Wright tomorrow and get the ball rolling. Obviously he'll be eager to wind this business up as quickly as possible."

"Eager is an understatement, I think he'll be desperate."

"In the next couple of weeks I'll probably have to take a few days holiday to attend executors' meetings in Glasgow and I think there should be a meeting with all the trustees and beneficiaries present, so we can all discuss it to make sure there are no misunderstandings. It's important the document is worded properly and everyone understands exactly what it entails."

"I don't have a problem with you taking part of your holidays to sort the will out."

Remarkably, over the next three weeks, we heard nothing from Rory or Peter, and when I queried Greg about this sudden breakdown in communications, he shrugged his shoulders.

"'The Law's Delays'. It's an old expression and very true. Lawyers often take an age to do things."

"But it's only a small law firm and I bet Rory will be pushing them along as hard as he can."

"As an executor, I'll be invited to the meeting when it's arranged."

The first we knew of the meeting was when the minutes arrived through the post. Greg was annoyed. Why hadn't he been invited? Even if Rory and my mother didn't know the procedure, and he was sure they did, Peter Wright must have known he had a duty to invite Greg.

"Are you not happy with the minutes? Is there something wrong with them?" I asked.

"There is no problem with the minutes, but that's not the point. They should have invited me, it's only common courtesy as I'm an executor, and they may have discussed subjects which they have failed to report in the minutes."

"I'll phone my mother tonight and ask her what she is playing at."

"You can if you want but it's closing the stable door after the horse has bolted."

I didn't have to phone her. She phoned me early that evening to ask if we had received the minutes and told me to contact Susanna as the documents we had to sign for the Deed of Arrangement had been sent to her address.

"Why didn't you invite Greg to the executors' meeting?"

"He's such a busy chap we didn't want to bother him."

"It's up to Greg to decide if he's too busy, not you."

"We were just thinking of him."

"Well try thinking of him as an executor next time, whose duty it is to attend executors' meetings. It's a real slap in the face for Greg after all he's done for Rory."

"Excuse me my dear, but you're going to benefit as well."

"I'm not the one who was in danger of losing my house and livelihood."

"Oh for Heaven's sake," she retorted, "we were just thinking of how inconvenient it would be for Greg to fly up to Glasgow."

"We'd already discussed it and he was quite prepared to fly up to Glasgow."

"Why do you have to be so difficult all the time?" she snapped back bad-temperedly.

This argument was going nowhere so I said nothing more; hopefully she'd got the message. I didn't want a row over the will or money.

Obediently, I phoned Susanna and suggested she and her family come to lunch with us on either Saturday or Sunday.

Neither day was convenient for them; we would have to go to Petersfield the following Sunday. We could come for lunch if we wanted, but we'd have to leave by 3pm.

Susanna greeted us with a cold haughtiness as we arrived.

"I'll show you the house," she said, as though that was the reason we had driven down.

I could feel the pride, only a fool would not have noticed it, as she strutted through the endless rooms in an aura of 'I am very rich', showing off her trophy, describing it with the selling skill an estate agent might employ as we filed round after her.

"This is the playroom, and over there is Dennis's office. That annex of the house is going to be a couple of spare bedrooms with en-suite bathrooms for guests." Click, click, click, her heels tapping on the floors as the guided tour progressed up the stairs, a computer room for the children, the nanny's room. Down the back stairs and into the over-sized garden.

The meal, to which Dennis had given us the warmest invitation only a few months earlier, was not an experience of easy-going affability. Susanna's new role didn't lend itself to easy chit-chat over the lunch table, so along with the food she also presented us with a general feeling of unfriendliness. They were both distant and unresponsive. I suppose you could argue that at least there was no pretence, no false charm, not much fun either. By the end of the meal I felt sorry for them.

Greg had attempted to discuss and explain the advantages and pitfalls of a Deed of Arrangement, but with their children and our child present it was difficult to hold much of a conversation. They both seemed uninterested and pretty vague about the whole thing. Some grubby little money-making scheme they were selflessly complying with seemed to be the general tone.

"If it'll help Rory, why not?" Susanna had said.

"It should help all of you, not just Rory," Greg answered.

A couple of their friends drove over after lunch to witness our signatures and, as the friends left, so did we.

"That's it then, we just wait for the money. I wonder how long it will take," I said, trying to put the best spin on what had been a horrendous lunch.

Greg was grim-faced; an unpleasant thought was turning in his mind. A casual remark from Dennis was ringing alarm bells.

"Why shouldn't she keep the money? It's not that much." Dennis had commented to Greg. "Perhaps it's not that much to him when his father's doling out hundreds of thousands in his direction," said Greg. "I can't imagine he'd be so cavalier if he were making his own way in life."

"It was only a flippant throw-away remark. Don't read so much into things."

"I felt like tearing up the whole document when he said that."

"If you were worried why didn't you say something?"

"Think how that would have made me look. It was my suggestion in the first place. Everyone else has signed it and then I refuse to. What does that say?"

"You can't trust my mother? Greg that's a terrible thing to say! I know I've never got on with her particularly well, but she is completely straight when it comes to money. I think it's horrible what you are implying. I bet my family are a lot straighter than yours when it comes to money," I said angrily. It had been a rotten lunch and now he was giving me this.

"Well thanks a lot," he snapped back, "you're telling me your mother will definitely give you your inheritance?"

"Why shouldn't she? You told me yourself she's got more than enough money. If you've any problems you can talk to her on Thursday when she comes to stay."

I don't think he would have said anything. As it was he didn't have a chance, she was on a charm offensive. The whole evening Greg listened with growing self-consciousness, wincing as Jane poured out her gratitude.

"Gus was such a good judge of character. He told me on a number of occasions, if, as a widow, I ever had any financial problems, I should ask your advice. How right he was."

"If you think I can be of help, please ask me. I'll be happy to give you my opinion."

"You've no idea what a tremendous relief this is to Rory. He was really depressed about the situation. You hear of estates being virtually wiped out by the time the Revenue have taken their whack and the legal bills have been paid. You take out loans to cover expenses and the banks charge fancy interest rates and before you know it you're paying interest on interest, all because the lawyers can't agree with the revenue on the valuation the auctioneers have put on the land. I'm not exaggerating; Rory and Phillipa were close to despair. The lawyers had warned them there could be a lot of complications with the revenue and they had visions of it dragging on for years. The end of this terrible period is entirely due to your ingenuity and wisdom."

"I was only doing what Gus asked me to do. Another person might well have come up with the same solution."

"Oh no, no. Jimmy Geddes thinks you're brilliant. He thinks it's a stroke of genius."

So Rory's troublesome time was over and Greg, the hero of the hour, cringed with the praise being heaped on his shoulders, as time and again Jane exclaimed.

"You've been such a godsend. Where would we be without you?"

She asked us if we'd like to go on holiday with her in the middle of May.

"When Scotland is at its nicest, and by then the estate will be wound up and perhaps Greg, you could advise me on what to do with my capital."

So it was arranged. The three of us would spend a week in St Andrews, as we had done last year when my parents decided they would like to get to know their grandson a little better.

Rory phoned a couple of weeks before our holiday and asked to speak to Greg. I only heard Greg's half of the conversation.

"Yes I'd enjoy a round of golf; I'll bring my clubs up with me."

"Will your mother mind if we leave St Andrews a day early to stay at Torlochan?"

"Well if you've discussed it with her and she's happy I can't see there is a problem," accompanied by some laddish laughter.

"Yes Rory, I'd like that. Thanks for asking us."

It smacked of, I don't know what. The arrogance of Rory. The obsequiousness of Greg, full of ready acceptance, as though he was Rory's little poodle, all polite and grateful to him for this kindness.

I was infuriated. As soon a he put the phone down I turned on him.

"How can you?" I fumed. "You know exactly what he thinks of us, and you in particular. Are we to believe his feelings towards us have altered overnight and for proof he's offering us a meal and a game of golf with you. Pretending to court our friendship after all this time. And what do you do? Yes Rory, I'd like that. Thanks for asking us," I minced, mimicking his words maliciously. This was a new tack from Rory and I didn't like it.

"If the boot had been on the other foot Rory would have considered the invitation a joke and wouldn't have wasted any time turning you down."

"I don't understand you. Sometimes you complain because your family ignores you, and now when your brother suggests he and I have a game of golf together and invites us both for a meal you complain even more."

"Do you honestly think for one moment Rory wants to be friends with people like us, and are you interested in being friends with him?"

"I think it's his way of saying thank you for helping sort out the problems of the will, don't you? I think you know that's why he's invited us, besides it would have made me look very rude if I hadn't accepted. You know quite well I like having the odd round of golf, and you or your mother certainly aren't going to have a round with me."

"And how do you think Henry is going to see this? Like a real kick in the teeth I imagine. He sees us as his friends, it'll seem like treason to him."

"Don't be ridiculous. Henry gets on with you and Susanna, even though you two always clash."

"That's different."

So we drove to Scotland with the golf clubs, and I tried to forget about next Saturday evening at Torlochan

Chapter 7

We reached the house late on Saturday afternoon and almost before we'd crossed the threshold Jane was telling us that she was off to visit Fiona the next day and there was a distant cousin's funeral on the Wednesday she had to attend. Making tiredness her excuse, she disappeared to bed smartly after supper, and we barely saw her on the Sunday. On Monday she made so little effort to be friendly, sometimes moving out of a room almost as soon as we'd entered as though trying to keep out of our way. We felt as though she didn't want us there. As the week wore on I had the sense she was wretchedly unhappy. We tried to talk to her but she was vague and distracted, as though trying to solve a complex problem that was playing on her mind. Sometimes when we spoke to her she failed to respond at all, and on other occasions she'd break off mid-sentence, as though totally unaware she'd done so. What problem did she have that could absorb her so completely? There was a profound nervousness about her, which I took a couple of days to notice, then I understood. After the initial trauma of bereavement the reality of facing up to a life of widowhood that stretched before her was frightening.

I'd seen her unhappy before. When each of her parents had died there had been what I can only describe as an open sadness, a different type of sadness. Crying, needing to talk of her loss. Commenting on the coincidence that Ann's death had been at the same age as her mother's, remarking on how she missed Douglas even though he'd become a cantankerous old man of late. He'd always been there for her if she needed him. She'd relate happy events of their past, remembering strange quirks of their personalities, such as we all have, and smiling nostalgically as she did so. Normally she was a woman who wore her heart on her sleeve; in a crisis she was the type that needed to constantly discuss the cause of her anxiety, her worry, her grief, whatever the problem. Now she was different from how I'd ever seen her. This must be the manifestation of some form of deep, delayed depression.

Depression, it must be depression. Immediately after my father's death she had been immersed in the financial practicalities of death. Everyone had marvelled at how well she'd coped. Now it was over, she was redundant. It was her time for grieving, coming to terms emotionally with bereavement. She had retreated beyond our reach. Occasionally she did talk to us. Dredging up morbid stories of destitute widows, friends' children who had lost everything in a murky divorce and turned to alcoholism, families with disabled children, embellishing every story with depressing asides. That was just after her four-year-old nephew had died of some rare form of blood cancer.

On the Thursday morning we sat on a bench by the beach watching Alex gather seaweed. He needed a fair amount as he intended to build a seaweed castle. I know most children build sandcastles, but he liked to be different and I felt I shouldn't suppress this creativity. We created openings for Jane to discuss her finances; after all this was ostensibly the reason she had invited us to spend the week with her. Hadn't she insisted that it was Greg's opinion in financial matters she most valued and how grateful she would be for his suggestions? Only a couple of months ago she'd appeared sincerely interested in his views, put such weight on his advice. Now she shunned any discussions on finance, as though it was distasteful and crass to discuss such matters on holiday.

It was a stranger we were with, her thoughts always returning to miserable, dreary stories, as though she was determined to be unhappy. I could not understand what message she was sending out from these convoluted tales. This wasn't a holiday; it was an endurance test of unrelenting misery and depression, her depression spoiling everything.

It wasn't until the supper on Friday, after Greg and Rory's round of golf, that she allowed herself to take an interest in what was being said. During the meal Rory regaled us with wretched stories of fellow farmers, unable to make ends meet, forced to sell farms that had been in the families for generations, of an acquaintance of his who had deliberately driven himself over a hillside so his family could benefit from his life assurance. A tenant farmer who had gone out to shoot rabbits and turned the gun on himself; we were told of how, as a result of a family dispute over Lord Lovat's estate, it had eventually dwindled to a fraction of its original size. Rory was at it too, feeding Greg and me a diet of harrowing tales.

I decoded the message in the subtext. If I didn't invest my money in the farm there would be dire consequences. Rory would turn to alcoholism and shoot himself. Oh, the delicate art of playing for high stakes; was he under the illusion he could pull at my heart-strings and the money would follow? Tough, we could all play at that game.

My mother, listening to him, lost the element of what now appeared like hostility.

"Did you enjoy the golf or were you too busy discussing other things?" Jane asked casually as the meal ended.

"We just concentrated on the golf." Rory answered the question with a shade too much emphasis.

I glanced up quickly, somehow sensing the undercurrents. It was only a glimpse, a cameo that passed rapidly across my mother's face; a moment later I would have missed it. A look of intense annoyance as her lips curled in tightly on themselves, while she gazed back at Rory. There was something in the anger of her expression, the complicity flying between them, which sent alarm bells ringing. As soon as supper was over Rory left and I wasn't sorry to see him go, hoping that tomorrow at Torlochan his conversation would be more-light hearted. I put Alex to bed for the night and wandered into the sitting room, where there was a serious discussion going on, which stopped abruptly the moment I entered. Greg, perched uncomfortably on the edge of a chair, stood up and walked away with his back to me.

"Go out and practise those shots you wanted to practise on the golf course," Jane instructed him, and without waiting for a response she immediately sparked up an animated conversation with me, the way she did when trying to put a nervous dinner party guest at ease. This friendly familiarity that had been absent all week sparked up a feeling of intense discomfort in me. I waited on tenterhooks for an answer to this unexpected show of chattiness. I now felt the distracted coolness easier to cope with than this unaccountable charm. Were these the overtones admitting us to the family? Was this what I had been longing for all week? And now, on its abrupt occurrence, I didn't like it. While I marked time in nervous anticipation it felt discordant. She had been playing the distressed widow and now the tempo had changed for no obvious reason and I was out of tune, in the wrong key. My mind could not adjust to this lively melody for fear she would return to the sombre rhythm and I would foolishly be playing a jig on my own.

Lacking the courage to ask the reason for this sudden change or perhaps seeing no point in asking, knowing her skill at side-stepping awkward questions, I made my excuses and returned to our bedroom. She was in a state of high agitation as I left. Was she annoyed that I could not respond to this unforeseen change in her mood? I felt guilty as I left her alone in the sitting room in the still of the early evening. What had she and Greg discussed to produce this metamorphic change? It was only a matter of minutes before Greg came storming into the bedroom in a furious state.

"Do you know what your mother's done? What does she think she is playing at? I can't believe it. She told me she is keeping the money that you signed over to her in the 'Deed of Arrangement'." The words came out like a series of explosions, fast, rapid and loud, leaving me reeling.

I laughed, not laughter of amusement, a hollow, empty laugh that suddenly explained so much.

"You don't understand how serious this is, think about it, just think about it for a minute, do you not realise what this all means?" Greg turned on me.

My laugh was no more than a simper now as I gazed back at him.

"Are you sure? What did she say to you?" were the first words I could think of.

"She said the money was legally hers and she was going to keep it."

"She doesn't need the money; we both know that, she is very well provided for. Why did she say that?" I demanded to know, in a horrified voice.

"I asked her what she intended doing with it. She told me she hadn't decided yet and that she was still thinking about it. It was said in such a tone it was clear she had no intention of discussing it with me any further. You know the emphatic way she speaks when she puts on that grand air, and then you came into the room."

"My God, are you sure?" I was appalled, I couldn't believe what I had heard, yet I had no reason to believe Greg had lied; surely he would not make such an error? It was not in his nature to be a trouble-maker and I was forced against my wishes to believe what he said was true.

I'd thought they wanted me to invest my money in the farm; instead they were investing it in the farm themselves.

"This was my worst fear. I knew we could never trust Rory, but you assured me your mother was honest over money. I knew as soon as we'd signed the Deed of Arrangement we were completely dependent on your mother behaving properly."

"At no time has it ever entered my mind that she wished to keep my share of the inheritance. I thought she was trying to persuade me to invest the money in George Cramer's road haulage business."

Her strange behaviour and tangled philosophy of the last week had confused me. Her unusual nervousness, her strange withdrawn manner and her reluctance to be in our company, how could I have failed to make the connection? Now it all seemed so obvious to me. I had made allowances for her unusual ways, thinking that delayed grief was the cause; indeed hoping that after a period of mourning our relationship might yet become close.

Now the true reason for the change in her behaviour had been exposed. Hidden behind the veil of widowhood she was worried about how to tell me, or rather us, of her change of mind, if that is what it was. For now, as I looked back, I suspected that this malicious plan had been hatching for many months behind the screen of grief. I, like a complete fool, had been taken in. The camouflage had worked. The cover had served its purpose. Now she could reveal all and present us with a *fait accompli*. There was no longer any need to conceal the trickery.

Enlightened as we were now with this horrendous revelation our minds swirled with their acts of deception. My mother's supposed grief, Rory's phoney friendship, the first ever invitation to supper tomorrow evening, the tragic stories of fellow farmers failing to cope with the commercial realities of farming, an indication no doubt, of his problems and a crude attempt to gain our sympathy and by this means make his, and my mother's behaviour more palatable.

"What can we do?" I whimpered pathetically, aghast as the realisation of this stupefying blow left me numb. How could my mind function when a bombshell like this landed, made worse as the recognition dawned that presumably my whole family was part of this coolly calculated and intentional deception. I felt utterly betrayed.

"Let's talk about it in the morning. I think we're both in a state of shock at the moment."

I couldn't understand why I awoke in better spirits than I'd been in all week. Perhaps because at last I understood the reason for my mother's bizarre behaviour. Greg was awake before me, resting his head against the headboard, cupping his chin in one hand as he did when thinking hard. Lying in bed we talked over and over the dilemma we found ourselves in.

"If it was my mother I would talk to her, ask her exactly what she was up to. I'd like to know why she didn't say something before the Deed of Arrangement was signed. Legally she was entitled to keep a third of the estate for herself, if she so wished. OK, I know there would have been a lot more tax to pay and it would have been more work for the lawyers and subsequently more legal expenses, but that would have been the correct way to behave if she wasn't happy with the arrangements. Really you should talk to her Jenny. It's your money she is intending to hold on to. If it was my mother that's what I would do."

"Can you imagine me talking to her? She's been trying to avoid talking to me all week. What would I say to her? Why don't we just continue as though nothing's happened, like we did last year when Rory and Phillipa decided at the last moment they'd had a better offer for dinner and went to the Stones' instead of coming to St Andrews as arranged. I was upset at their rudeness, but you persuaded me to ignore their behaviour and be polite, behave as though nothing had happened, and you were right, that was the best advice."

"You don't understand how serious this is. It isn't a case of rude or ignorant behaviour. This is deceit. They've broken their word, violated an agreement, albeit verbal, and now you're being cheated out of your inheritance. You can't just stand by and do nothing. You have to fight for it, and you can't let Rory and your mother get away with this. There is no way I'm going for a meal at Torlochan tonight. It would be horrendous, knowing all the time that, while your brother and his wife are wining and dining us, they are laughing up their sleeve, congratulating themselves on the clever trick they've pulled off. The very thought of it makes me shudder. The food would stick in my throat."

Eventually we decided that I would tell my mother we intended to drive straight to Henley as that would give us the whole of Sunday to recover and prepare for work on Monday.

"I think you should go and talk to her about her change of heart over your money at the same time," Greg urged. "I've been wracking my brains all night and two things I know. She's clearly doing this for Rory, not for herself; and she's not stupid. She knows what she is doing is wrong, that's why she been withdrawn and strange all week. You must talk to her and persuade her to see your point of view."

"I'll play it by ear as to whether I say anything about the will. Whatever we do we're in a no-win situation. I know she has us down as greedy, but she doesn't know which sort of greedy. Long-term greedy, where we keep quiet about what they've done and hope for a big payout when she dies, or short-term greedy, and kick up a fuss now."

"What do you want to do? You must decide."

"If I leave things as they are it'll make me look weak and greedy and as I'll definitely lose the inheritance from Daddy as well."

"That's true."

"And there is no guarantee Mummy would include me in her will, in fact she might argue that, as we hadn't complained about what they've done this time, I'm not that bothered about her will."

"I think, by law, half her estate has to be divided between her children, so you would at least be entitled to a twelfth."

"She could give away most of her money before she dies."

"There is nothing to stop her doing that."

"If I kick up a fuss it's going to be unbelievably unpleasant. I hate having disagreements over money at the best of times and this just couldn't be worse."

"I agree with you."

"On the other hand they knew exactly what they were up to. The only thing they don't know is which way the cat is going to jump."

"I can hear her in the kitchen, why don't you go and talk to her now."

I dressed quickly and walked through to the kitchen, bracing myself for a row. Technically it was her money. In the eyes of the law it was her money, but morally it was mine.

She stood at the sink with her back to me, silhouetted against the bright, early-morning June sun, as it streamed in through the large window in front of her. Framed by the architrave, as though a centrepiece in a picture, her shoulders hunched a shade more than usual, her head drooping, contributing to the air of despondency as she washed last night's dishes, sullenly, silently, conveying her displeasure at my slovenly forgetfulness. A mute reprimand that echoed at full volume. I hadn't completed my evening chores.

She froze for a moment as I entered the kitchen, her hands thrust deep into the soapy water, her gaze obstinately fixed at the sink, then she slowly continued as dish after dish was washed, rinsed, stacked, washed, rinsed, stacked with a depressingly slow deliberate rhythm. No greeting, no acknowledgement of my arrival in the kitchen, just the ferocious silence as she continued her task, an ordeal undertaken with an air of weary martyrdom for my unfinished task. The note had changed from last night. Gone was the false gaiety. Now the air was full of sullen petulance. Although all I had seen was the back of her head, it was quite clear she was in no mood for discussions. I told her quickly of our change of plans. The uncomfortable silence continued as I waited for her response.

Unexpectedly, she turned round from the sink and, for the first time that morning, she looked at me straight in the face. A sharp electric shock of discomfort shot through my body, and I winced with a moment's pang. The skin around her eyes was mottled and raspberry red, her eyes swollen and bloodshot, as the tears continued to roll down her cheeks. It was not what I expected, but in the aftermath of the initial shock my feelings turned quickly to cynicism at this display of emotion. I stared back at her in a cold stony silence.

"You've no idea how I miss your father." She seemed to snarl.

I said nothing as I looked at her. I'm sure she did miss my father, but this display of grief from her, the first for the whole week, was not for him. These tears were a mockery, part of some greater performance in the worst of situations; this affected anguish over the death of my father serving as blanket to hide her deception and at the same time to be used as a tool to castigate me, to manipulate me for Rory's purposes.

She dried her hands briskly on the kitchen towel and stormed out of the room, refusing to look in my direction again as I watched speechless. She was in no mood to discuss the will.

"She must have been brooding all week over the way we would react to her duplicity and now she realises there's going to be trouble," Greg said, emerging from the bedroom with Alex.

"What can I say to her when she behaves like this? Isn't this behaviour confirmation of everything you told me last night? She might not have said much this morning. Nevertheless she's sent out plenty of signals, and to me it's blindingly obvious she's made up her mind and she's clearly in no mood for a rational discussion. Do you honestly think she is going to change her stance if I talk to her? She's laid down the gauntlet and we're in a no-win situation."

"Now is the best time to talk to her, that I'm sure of."

"I thought I spoke to her very politely then. I never even mentioned the will and look how she responded."

"Leave her till after we've had breakfast and talk to her again. Perhaps she'll tell you I misunderstood what she said last night."

"Do you think you did?"

"No, but if she says I did I'll accept it."

"Why don't you talk to her then?"

"I don't think you realise just how serious this is? You're her daughter and you're entitled to the inheritance your father wanted you to have. I am an executor, who was appointed to sort out the financial side of the will, which I think I have done, so my part in this business is over."

"As an executor aren't you still involved, don't you have a duty to ensure my father's wishes are carried out? Or at least that the spirit of the will is adhered to?"

"I don't think it's my place to talk to her. Through you I am indirectly a beneficiary, which puts me in a very awkward position if I kick up a fuss over the way your mother has decided to keep the money."

"I'm not talking to her. I know what she's like and she's not going to change her mind."

"She might not, as you say, but you should give her the chance to. I can't believe she wants a row."

"I'm frightened she'll just shout at me."

I decided the best course of action was to leave quickly, putting as much distance as possible between my mother and myself, but not until after breakfast. It was a miserable meal, neither of us having much of an appetite, but I for one was not prepared to set off on a four hundred mile journey on an empty stomach. We tidied up a bit and packed the car, then in the most agonising discomfort returned to say goodbye to my mother. She emerged from the bedroom, still in tears, laced with the kind of angry defiance best seen in a spoilt child who still has not got its way. As she held her cheek out to me, I forced myself, I don't know how I managed, to give her a kiss, and as I did so she pulled a handkerchief from her pocket and ran back to the room in an Oscar-winning demonstration of sorrow, as a fresh flood of tears appeared.

And that was how I left her. She had taken a gamble, uncertain as to which path I would take, whether I'd shrug off the loss of my inheritance and turn a blind eye to her deception, anxious not to upset the bereaved widow. How could I have a row with her over money, at such a time, when all she was doing was her best to help her hardworking, disadvantaged sons. I, in return for a magnanimous act, or a humanitarian gesture towards my greedy brother, was being offered friendship with Rory and Phillipa, a meal with them tonight, a place for Greg and myself in the bosom of the family.

As soon as we emerged from the drive and hit the road south, I let loose a laugh, a deep, full-bodied, triumphal laugh. Was it release of tension after the last twelve hours or finally the undeniable proof of what I had often stated?

"I always told you she didn't like me very much. Do you believe me now?"

"Did you ever for a moment think she would do this?"

"You know quite well I didn't. I would never have agreed to sign the Deed of Arrangement if I thought for a moment she would do this. She's always portrayed herself as one who is morally superior, straight with money, always prepared to be up front and open and speak her mind whatever the consequences. I'm the offender, weak-willed and pathetic, liable to go off the rails without proper spiritual guidance. Your suspicions at Susanna's house were right; I think she intended to stitch us up from the start to keep my share of the money."

"You were adamant she wouldn't do any thing underhand, 'It wasn't her style,' you said. Whatever she was, she was straight with money. Imagine how bad it would have made me look if I'd refused to sign the deed, especially as it was my idea initially. She is making use of her widowhood to get her own way. I've been of service to her and, now she no longer needs me, she can cast me off."

We talked of nothing else on the long journey back, not then realising how this topic would monopolise our lives for months to come.

Chapter 8

When the shock had sunk in and the anger surfaced, the enormity of it hit me. Perhaps it was listening to Greg, stunned and distressed because of my brother and mother.

"What did I do wrong? I only wanted to help. Why has she done this?" he said over and over again.

It wasn't that Greg hadn't supported me in my fracas with Jane in the past, he just hadn't been directly in the firing line and there had never been a bolt of this magnitude before.

"Peter Wright must have guessed something like this would happen, perhaps he understands your mother's personality better than I do. That was why he never suggested a 'Deed of Arrangement'."

"I never dreamt my mother would do this."

"It's Rory. I knew we could never trust Rory, but I never thought your mother would be party to anything so base."

"That brother of mine, you'd think he'd show some gratitude to you, for saving his life."

"You're being melodramatic."

"O.K. Not his life, but you saved his career as a farmer."

"Don't worry; I never expected gratitude from him. Even though the lawyers didn't suggest the Deed of Arrangement, someone else could have come up with the idea."

"Like who?"

"I don't know. Look at Roger. He sets up 'Deeds of Arrangement' day in and day out."

"Come on, if it wasn't for you the idea would never have been unearthed and Rory would have been crippled financially. Wasn't it Daddy's wish that Rory should continue farming if possible? Surely this was the only solution to the problem."

"Yes, I thought so at the time."

"Who could have foreseen this?"

And so we talked on and on, round and round in endless circles. There wasn't a mealtime when we didn't agonise over the dreadful turn of events. Out for a run in the car, at lunchtime when Greg phoned and in bed we discussed it. Watching television we tried not to talk about it, but we still thought about it. Could Greg have misunderstood Jane? If only I'd had the courage and spoken to her directly about the will on that last morning.

I tortured myself, knowing how she operated in these situations. Believing the best form of defence is attack, the assault would now be well in progress. I could visualise her resplendent in her new role of widowhood, playing the martyr, a part she'd perform to perfection. It would be no effort to present her story in a sympathetic light. The callous treatment of a bereaved widow, by the grasping selfishness of her daughter over her late father's will. She'd always had misgivings about my character, indeed hadn't the doctors confirmed her suspicions many years ago, but anything as abhorrent as my present conduct had never entered her mind. Could any one imagine a more grim example of turning to bite the hand that feeds you? If people believed her, as I believed people did, it was horrible, unbelievably horrible. How could she be so cruel, so unjust?

"Whatever she's saying about you, it won't be half as bad as what she's saying about me," Greg would remonstrate.

What did she hope to achieve by disclosing the cross she had to bear? Compassion I suppose; she must have fostered a lot of that amongst her friends and family. At a time when she deserved comfort and kindness from me, I was displaying an unnatural brutality; perhaps a form of hysteria brought on by the true nature of my greedy and selfish character. It was all so obvious to her now. My mother would enjoy exhibiting these fabricated accounts of my behaviour, portraying my personality as it suited her to see it, soliciting the sympathy and commiserations of everyone, for who could fail to be appalled on hearing such a frightful tale? I could imagine them listening aghast, for told in this light it was indeed a hideous story. She would be in her element, sustained by their depth of horror and their admiration for her strength of character. Only what did she hope this bizarre behaviour would achieve?

How could I ever return to Torlochan knowing the excellent job my mother was performing? This public exposé of Greg's and my despicable personalities, not only said but believed. How could I face any one of my family or their friends? Ironically, I knew that what I longed for was her approval, her good opinion, her love.

Why couldn't she write to me, with some justification, anything. One letter of explanation, she'd been blinded by grief, confused as anyone would be. Rory had put her under tremendous pressure. She hadn't considered the consequences of what she was doing. She didn't think I would be so hurt. I prayed for the letter that never came.

Nothing I could do would shake off the terrible agony. At night in the silence I wept in the dark, my tears and sobs lost in the pillow until the Sandman swept me into the land of Nod. Even here in my sleep, the turmoil of my days reappeared, heavy with sorrow. I could not shake off this sadness that clung to me, haunted me, pursued me in my dreams. I cried her name over and over, "Mummy, Mummy."

Until one morning, in the early hours, I awoke cold and startled. It was the dream that still cursed me, preying on my waking mind. The cries 'Mummy, Mummy' recurring eerily from outside the room, carried over from my dreams. It must be a dream, dreaming I was awake while I was still asleep, unable to wake up. I'll wake up and the nightmare will pass, but I was awake, I knew I was awake. I lay frightened; my mind was playing a cruel trick. I was going mad. I lay in a cold sweat, numb with fear and trepidation. "Mummy, Mummy." Those childish cries, those cries from my dream continued, unrelenting. I could only lie and shake with frightened awareness that finally my sanity had left me. Slowly reality filtered through the drowsiness of a disturbed dream. "Mummy, Mummy," Alex was crying my name. I got up and walked through to his room. My child was crying. I was the mummy. Those unguarded nocturnal cries from Alex, jolting me into a bizarre role-reversal as from the child in my dream crying for my mother. Correspondingly, I became the mother in my child's dream as he cried for me. This surreal night-time experience, reality intermingling with my dreams, rattled me badly.

The misery that followed the nights into the days, creating the urge to talk and talk of the mischief, the wrongdoing, the injustice, was compelling. It offered a form of release; as though by talking I could somehow extricate myself from the stress of the events, for I was so deeply marked I could hardly sustain a conversation of any nature other than my present crisis. My distraction was an obsession as I was driven to disclose my circumstances to anyone who would lend an ear. Many kind souls spent hours listening, surprised and appalled at my disturbing tale, offering sympathy. Others would give cries of disbelief and wince uncomfortably at the vulgarity of washing one's dirty linen in public, unwilling to hear such unsolicited personal revelations. Contravening the rules of good behaviour amongst well-bred ladies, this wasn't done.

For some, the justification of sudden bereavement was reason enough to behave in an uncharacteristic manner, and if my whole family were against me, surely the fault must lie at my feet. Friends I'd known for years were mystified at what they considered my irrational reaction, gently reminding me that Jane and I had always had a stormy relationship. For some reason I took these remarks with the greatest offence. Had I not told them of the new bond that had formed between us? How Jane had become fond of me, and valued Greg, as Gus had once done. I even felt compelled to explain it all to visiting customers. Attempt to muster their support so they understood my position, forcing them to listen to this sordid tale, when all they'd only wanted was a quote for a new pair of bedroom curtains.

As the weeks passed our conversations were plagued by her actions. Like a record that had got stuck in a groove, we went over and over and over the same events, as though constant repetition could flush out the problem. Did she know what she was doing? Was it nothing more than a terrible misunderstanding? It wasn't, until Alex returned late one afternoon after visiting a friend down the road, asking. "What does this mean, Mummy?" and, as he spoke, he pointed his index finger to his temple and moved it in a circular motion, the way one does when indicating someone may be slightly unhinged.

"Why?" I replied

"Because Tara's mummy told her daddy you were." And he repeated the action.

I felt my stomach lurch as shades of *déjà vu* raised their ugly heads.

"Oh that," I said airily, "it means I'm very jokey."

I may be able to fool him at the moment, but soon he'd know exactly what it meant. Children are cruel enough to each other as it is; did I really need to make life more difficult for him? Coming two days after my phone call to the book club, it felt like a double whammy, unexpectedly seeing both sides of the coin.

Greg's sister-in-law, Rhona, is ten years older than I am, and if I can put it tactfully, she enjoys her food. After a recent medical check at a Well Woman clinic, the nurse had been quite ruthless. She must alter her diet immediately; a sample of her blood had proved that her cholesterol level was far too high, she was a prime candidate for a heart attack if she didn't alter her diet immediately. The book club, which I belonged to, advertised a low-level cholesterol cookbook and I had read a favourable review of the book's recipes. Feeling virtuous I thought I'd order a book for Rhona. I knew it would only take a minute. Credit card in hand, I dialled the number. A Liverpudlian lady answered the phone and I told her the code.

"Oh, that's the low cholesterol book isn't it?" she enquired.

"Yes," I answered, assuming she was being professional and checking I'd ordered the correct book.

"Have you got problems with high cholesterol levels yourself?" she asked.

"No." I answered briskly, wondering if some kind of survey was being conducted.

"I have," she told me. "Terribly high cholesterol level I've got. I think it happened after the change. The doctor told me these things often do. I'm not a bit overweight." She droned on telling me about the H.R.T. treatment she'd been given and how her husband had died very suddenly and she wondered if it might have been the shock that had upset her balance and pushed up her cholesterol level.

I wasn't interested; I only wanted to order the book. *We've all got problems, you stupid woman. Do you think I want to hear about yours? We just have to get on with our lives,* I wanted to say to her; instead, I sat mutely and watched my fingers drumming on the table in irritation. I had other things to do than listen to this waffling. What was it about the drumming fingers? I knew it would come back to me. I tried to remember. I blushed as the recollection came to me. I'd seen the teacher at Alex's nursery school the previous week do it as I explained my own personal problems to her.

In all the weeks my mind had been wrapped up in my own concerns, I had never considered how others would see me. I'd only needed them to understand so they could give me sympathy and support, like the garrulous saleswoman at the book club needing an ear to listen to her troubles.

It was a shocking revelation, as though I'd walked into a kaleidoscope and was seeing unappealing reflections of myself from different angles. I didn't like the images. No wonder people were thinking that I was deranged! From now on in public I must try to behave like the kind of woman I aspired to be, easy-going and calm. However, within the confines of the house, the intense pain festered. Poor Greg, somewhere along the way I lost the plot and I took my anger out on him the way I could not take it out on anyone else. He was an easy target. Some trivial, throw-away remark and I would launch into an angry tirade.

"What do you mean, 'people are basically decent'? People are basically cruel. My family are people, educated people at that, lawyers, accountants, teachers. How many people are there in my family? Count them, siblings, their spouses, aunts, uncles, cousins. At least thirty, maybe forty, and not one of them has given me a word of support over this business. So don't go telling me people are basically decent, because they're not."

"Didn't you realise everything depended on your mother behaving honourably? Surely you knew your family would always support her."

"No I didn't. Call me naïve, but I thought at least one of them would have had the backbone to stand up to her."

"You've always been an outsider in your family. You never toed the party line. Did you honestly expect anyone to stick their neck out for you now?"

"Yes I did," I'd cry in despair.

"Don't worry, we'll be alright. Look at Alex. You've got to think of him; he gives you pleasure doesn't he? Now you're having another baby, think how happy you'll be with two children." Greg always comforted me this way. I was to look forward, think of all the good things life had to offer. "Your mother is the real loser in all this if only she could see it. She is not going to see her grandchildren, and how can she live with herself, knowing what she's done? You would have been a comfort to her. Rory's going to want more from her, can she not see that? I'm the one who will be really demonised in this matter. I can just imagine your mother complaining about my council house background."

Every word he said rang true, I felt ashamed. I clung to him like a frightened child as he talked.

Chapter 9

He came storming into the house one night after work, more upbeat than I'd seen him for weeks

"I have it. I'll resign as executor. It seems such an obvious solution. Why has it taken me so long to come up with it?"

He wasn't even aware his mind was on this business, when suddenly the solution had burst upon him unexpectedly; he had found the key.

"I'll write to Peter Wright stating the fact that your mother is not carrying out your father's wishes as justification for my action. If she intends to carry out your father's wishes she can write back and tell me there has been a misunderstanding and I'll accept there will be no need for me to resign. I don't think I did misunderstand her, but this way the ball is in her court. If they accept my resignation we can take it as proof that they have deceived us or they can assure us they are going to distribute the money according to your father's wishes."

Dear Peter,

Gus MacKenzie's Estate

As you may or may not be aware, my mother-in-law, contrary to assurances she has given me in the past, has informed me that she has decided to keep money transferred to her through the Deed of Arrangement.

In these circumstances I feel I can no longer continue as executor to Gus MacKenzie's estate and can only express my deep regret that his wishes will not now be carried out. I have acted in the utmost good faith throughout this sorry affair.

Can you please send me the necessary documentation (if any) to enable me to resign? I have returned the documents you recently sent, as, for the reasons described above, I am unable to sign them.

Yours sincerely,

Greg.

Copied to Mrs Mackenzie

The message on the ansaphone was brief.

"Greg, it's Rory here. Phone me back. I want to talk to you."

It was obvious from the curt tone of his voice and the bluntness of the statement, coming the day after Greg had posted his letter of resignation that any discussion would be disagreeable and acrimonious.

"I'm not having an undignified row over the phone with your brother. If he's got anything to say to me he can put it in writing. Can you phone the lawyers tomorrow and ask them to pass the message on to him?"

It was over two weeks before we heard another word.

Dear Greg,

Mr Gus Mackenzie's Estate

I was absent from the office on holiday from the end of June until Tuesday of this week. On my return your letter of 21ˢᵗ July was placed before me and I was told that your mother-in-law had arranged an appointment to see me on Wednesday. I had no prior knowledge of anything which your mother-in-law had said to you.

When I met your mother-in-law on Wednesday she explained that when she said to you that she would have to allow for retaining some funds when calculating the amount which she could distribute among the family by way of a gift, she was not intending to express any departure from the ideas discussed at an earlier stage. Instead her intention was to point out that the funds which she would have available for gifting to the family (and these are largely funds which never formed part of Mr Mackenzie's estate as the estate is not going to produce sufficient liquid funds to cover £81,000.00 to be distributed among the family and the liabilities for income tax and capital gains tax incurred before the date of Mr Mackenzie's death but still outstanding at his death and therefore forming debts on his estate) would inevitably be reduced by the payments by her on behalf of the estate (which would have been debts of the estate if no Deed of Arrangement had been executed) such as the capital gains tax and income tax to which I have already referred, the provision of a headstone, and accounts paid to contractors instructed by Mr Mackenzie in connection with work in building the house carried out before the date of death. Apart from outlays such as these directly connected with and due from the estate, but funded by your mother-in-law, the only other payment which she intended to allow for when considering the net funds available for gifting among the family was the premium paid by her on the term assurance policy written in trust for the benefit of the family to cover the additional inheritance tax which would be payable if she were to die within seven years of having made gifts to the family.

As you appreciate my status is that I am a solicitor dealing with the administration of Mr Gus Mackenzie's estate on the instructions of his executors. As an incidental to that I am able to, and happy to, give advice on the possible tax consequences of one member of the family making gifts to others: but it is not my place to comment on discussions within the family as to the amounts of any gifts which might be made et cetera. I have simply passed on the explanation given to me by your mother-in-law in a sincere attempt to be helpful to all of you and in the sincere hope that it helps to resolve any difficulties or misunderstandings which have arisen.

In the meantime, to implement your express request, I have prepared a 'Minute of Resignation' and I enclose it. Please sign it at the end where your initials are marked. Please sign in the presence of two witnesses (not Jenny) and have the witnessess sign alongside where indicated adding the word 'Witness' after their signatures.

With kind regards,

Peter.

An ambiguous letter if ever there was one, managing to place the blame well and truly at our feet, making the vilest allegations concerning Greg. Meanwhile he was to resign, which, as maintained by his reasoning, meant she did not intend to carry out my father's wishes, while at the same time declaring her intentions to do exactly that.

"Your mother said no such thing that last evening at St Andrews. It's monstrous what she is saying about me. Any right thinking person would expect these expenses to come out of the estate."

"Peter Wright must know it's not true. He's written a disclaimer in the letter."

"Of course he does, it's preposterous. No professional person would make the remarks your mother is alleging I made."

We called on our neighbours that evening, and Greg, swearing he would never act as an executor for a will again, signed the document in their presence.

"You should write to your mother and ask her to explain exactly what she proposes to do," the neighbours suggested.

With Greg's help I wrote a letter the next day. It was essential for his job that he wrote letters couched in the words of business jargon, using the same language as the lawyers and accountants. I would have spent days going all round the houses and still not have said what I intended. He, like an arrow, went straight to the point, then, changing position, he would repeat the message from a different angle.

His secretary complained to him that his letters were full of repetitions. For this he made no apology. He was giving and explaining detailed financial advice.

"Money is a very emotive issue," he argued. "It doesn't matter if I repeat myself so long as I get the message over clearly, that's what is important. Not giving full explanations and advice, that is a problem."

Dear Mummy,

I am writing to you to clarify your intentions regarding the will.

As you know, to avoid substantial amounts of tax, the beneficiaries all signed a Deed of Arrangement transferring money to you, with you then agreeing to transfer the money to us in accordance with Daddy's wishes, which are that Rory is given the shares and that the rest of the estate is divided equally among the others. On the above basis I signed the Deed of Arrangement. For tax reasons the above could not be made legally binding.

At St Andrews you told Greg that:

1. The money transferred to you was legally yours and that you had confirmed this with Peter Wright.
2. That you intended to keep the money transferred to you.
3. You had not yet decided what to do with money transferred to you, as you had not thought that far ahead.

Greg of course was astonished when you said this as you had always led him to believe that all along you had intended to carry out Daddy's wishes. By making the above remarks you clearly indicated that you are not going to carry out Daddy's wishes.

As you know Greg has written to Peter Wright to resign as executor on the grounds that Daddy's wishes are no longer going to be carried out. Greg has now received a reply to suggest that:

1. All along you were going to carry out Daddy's wishes.
2. The only money you were going to keep was that relating to tax, house expenses, headstone and the policy and presumably the legal expenses although he did not mention these.

Regarding 2: This money was never going to be distributed for obvious reasons and Greg is amazed that you thought it could be distributed to the beneficiaries.

What you said to Peter Wright and what you have indicated to Greg are quite different. Can you please confirm for the record whether you intend to carry out Daddy's wishes?

I am sorry to have to write this letter, but I am very upset by this business and I want to find out where I stand with you.

It was Daddy's wish that I be given a share of his assets and I will find it unforgivable if you do not carry out his wishes.

Can you please respond in writing in order to ensure that there is no further misunderstanding regarding your intentions with respect to my inheritance?

Jenny.

Dear Jenny,

My mother has been too upset by Greg and your own behaviour to read your letter. Consequently I have forwarded it to Peter

Wright. All future correspondence from Greg and you will be addressed to him.

Rory.

It felt like a heavy punch in the stomach as I struggled to breathe normally. What was he playing at? The pain was so great I could only sit on the kitchen chair, as I rocked backwards and forwards hoping this action might somehow relieve the torment. These words recount my actions, none of which convey the true agony.

If we had done them a deep injustice they could not have been more cruel. All we had ever intended was to help and this was how they thanked us. Greg came into the kitchen and, looking at the letter, guessed at once the cause of my pathetic state. He took it from my hand and read it through once before falling heavily, as though buffeted, onto a kitchen chair. His eyelids clicked mechanically up and down, up and down, up and down, too fast for normality. He looked hurt. I thought he was blinking back the tears, but when he spoke it was anger that was the emotion he was trying to control. He shook his head violently like a wet dog shaking off the excess water after a swim and pulled himself together.

"Write this letter, write this letter now, take a copy and post it to Rory immediately. If he wants a fight that is fine by me." Greg's anger jolted me back from my anguish as he dictated the letter.

Dear Rory,

Thank you for your letter 27/7 and I note with great sorrow that my mother is too upset to respond to my letter. I also am greatly upset.

You mention that my mother has been upset by our behaviour. Can you please clarify this if you know the reason why? I am not aware that Greg or I have acted in any way improperly.

I trust you will not be too upset to respond to this letter.

Jenny.

"I'll post it this morning," I promised pathetically.

I couldn't cope with his anger at the moment.

"Jenny, your mother can't like you much. I know she didn't write this letter, but she must have seen it. Rory wouldn't write a letter like this without showing it to your mother first."

"I know; that is what upsets me so much. Before, Daddy always dealt with everything and she just went along with it. Now he is not there to restrain her, she and Rory are coping in their own peculiar way," I replied.

"This isn't coping, this is bullying. Rory could have passed all his and our letters through lawyers without telling us. We might have suspected, but we would have never have known for sure. Post that letter, first thing, we can't let that brother of yours bully us like this."

The tears came. I cried and cried. My whole body quivered with the force of my weeping as I'd never wept before. Greg held my hand as I wept, wiping the relentless tears with my other hand. He stayed until exhaustion took over, leaving me drained and powerless in the chair.

"I'll be all right," I whimpered, "you'd better go to the office, you're very late."

"I'll phone you at lunchtime," he promised.

"I can't believe this is happening to us. Why are they behaving like this?"

"I don't know, I don't know," Greg repeated.

He left for the office an hour later than usual. I could only perform the basics of child care, but the need to dress Alex, to feed him, to reassure him that I was alright, when I transparently wasn't, meant going through the motions of a normal day. My letter, dictated by Greg, was photocopied and posted with a terrible dread. What sort of response would it produce?

I felt my mind, already in turmoil, was being tortured more. The pains roused by the morning's letter battered my demoralised spirits. Weak and damaged I felt that at any moment now I would capsize and sink with the fierceness of the blow.

Would I ever recover and feel happy again? I reread the letter I had written to Jane three days ago. It was not friendly, neither was it aggressive; it was matter of fact. Whatever her interpretation of the letter I did not deserve the response I'd received this morning. There was no point contacting the lawyer. They would tell me to get lost, couched in courteous legal jargon, but the meaning would be the same.

Rory's letter had signalled to us the extent of his cruelty. We had been totally deceived and double-crossed, now we were being blamed as well. The support of my mother was of the utmost importance to Rory. If he could count on her endorsement, as Greg had pointed out, the others would unite behind her willingly. She would know her material worth and demand commitment. There may be a flutter of concern from Susanna, a twinge of conscience from Henry. Nothing that couldn't be overridden with a sensible talking to, and they'd bow down and toe the line, toe Rory's line. Once it was established Rory was in charge, affairs would be carried out his way with no questions asked; there would be little resistance to his iron will. He was not a man to be crossed.

Stupidly, I'd trusted that Jane had the integrity, the strength, the decency to stand up to Rory, but I was mistaken. How could I ever forgive them for what they had done? I could take no more; I wanted them out of my life forever. I wrote my next letter that afternoon, realising I had no choice; all my hopes of reconciliation with my mother were dashed. I had to take action, grab a lifeline to protect myself from sinking further.

Dear Mummy,

I feel unbelievably hurt at the way you've treated us. Greg did his best for you and would have been happy to continue to advise you, with your best interests at heart, not his, as you seem to imply. I feel your treatment of him as an executor has been shabby to say the least.

I'm sure my brothers and sisters all knew about your decision not to carry out Daddy's wishes, and I don't know why you could not have told me as well.

Isabel told me the night Daddy died that Phillipa was complaining about his will, and to go ahead and have a large housewarming party in his old house, only seven weeks after his death, is in poor taste and I am surprised it was allowed. Out of respect for Daddy I thought it would have been deferred. You have made complete fools of Greg and me. In view of the above and the comments you've made to Alan Wright about Greg I don't see how I can ever see you again.

I feel all this could have been avoided if you had been honest and open with us. I am truly sorry it has ended like this.

Greg and I are not worried about the money, but we would have liked an explanation as to why you could not carry out Daddy's wishes.

Jenny.

I showed it to Greg as soon as it was written.

"Don't post it yet, leave it a couple of days. She may write to you herself in a more conciliatory vein when she has had time to think about Rory's letter."

"That wasn't only Rory's letter. It's got her fingerprints all over it, and you said yourself that she must have seen it, Rory wouldn't post a letter like that without consulting Mummy."

"If I were you I'd leave it a few days."

"Well I'm not you, I can't take any more and I'm putting a stop to all this before I go mad, and, besides, I want to tell her to get lost before she tells me to."

"It's up to you."

That evening I posted it. There would be a response, she always had to have the last word, but in the interest of maintaining my sanity, that was my last word.

Chapter 10

The next morning a letter arrived.

Dear Greg,

Mr Gus Mackenzie's Estate

Thank you for your letter of 27th July returning the minute of Resignation duly signed and witnessed.
Thank you also for the kind comments, which I do appreciate. With good wishes.

Yours sincerely,

Peter Wright.

Before the day was over Greg called me from his office.

"I've just had a phone call from John Anderson. He told me your mother is at the end of her tether and feels like telling you she wants nothing more to do with you. I wasn't sure if he was calling my bluff or not, so I said to him, 'John, before you go any further I better tell you, Jenny has written a letter to that effect to her mother'. He immediately said, 'Don't let her post it'. I told him I was sorry, it was too late, you had posted it last night and your mother will get it tomorrow morning. Then he said, 'Oh my God, I'll phone you back', and put down the receiver."

"Did he say when he was going to phone back?"

"No, but I think we can assume he is phoning your mother right now."

"She won't like it that I've taken the initiative and told her I want to cut all ties. That's the role she likes to take."

"She probably wasn't expecting a second letter quite so soon either. I'd better go; he'll probably phone me back quite soon. I'll let you know what happens."

It happened very soon, not much longer than five minutes later.

"That's it. John's just phoned again and your mother's promised to pay us the money. Isn't that a relief, I can't believe it's been such hard work getting the money out of her."

"I don't know if I want it now. With all the heartache over this inheritance, I'd rather have nothing to do with them than have the money after the way they've treated me."

"The money is morally yours so you should take it."

"You're probably right, but I can't really take it in at the moment. Tomorrow my mother's going to receive my letter. What is she going to do then?"

"Well it's had the desired effect and it's not going to be a complete surprise to her."

What she did was phone Greg at the office the following day. Sure enough she'd received my letter and wanted to know if he agreed with everything that I had written? He told her he did. Even the part about never seeing her again? No he didn't agree with that part, but he agreed with everything else. She would send me the money, leave everything for a month to let things blow over, and then we'll just forget all about this debacle and never discuss the business again. That was how they left it, on her terms.

"Why did you tell her you didn't agree with the bit about not ever seeing her again? That was the prime sentiment of my letter, the only part of the letter that'll worry her and you tell her you don't go along with it and she'll assume I'll go along with what you say."

"What else could I say? Surely you can see what a difficult position it is for me? I can assure you I am in no hurry to see your mother, or any of your family again."

"Yes, I know it's awkward for you, but she has us now. She can behave as she likes, leave things a month and then never talk about her behaviour with us. In the meantime our name has been blackened."

"Well, she assures me she is going to give you the money. Once you've got it you may feel differently, because I'm sure you still like her despite all that's happened."

"What else was said?"

"I told her I refuse to have any further financial dealings with her, any of her other children, or any member of her family."

I gasped. "What did she say to that?"

"Nothing. What could she say?"

She was responding to my letter. By rights she should have phoned me, but she knew I would not have been so kind or let her off as lightly as Greg had done. She had laid down the guidelines and he had acquiesced. She'd reckoned on his non-confrontational nature to appease her, coupled with the recognition that his position in this affair was delicate, and the gamble had paid off. One thing was clear in my mind; she may wish never to mention the subject to Greg or to me, but knowing my mother, she'll have discussed it with plenty of other people, and what had been said would not be forgotten; it just wouldn't be mentioned in our presence. The whispering and the covert remarks would reverberate round the family. The skeleton in the cupboard would rattle every time my name was mentioned. *You know how badly she behaved over her father's will, and poor Jane, as though she didn't have enough problems, without Jenny making a fuss over a few thousand pounds. It's not as though she even needs the money.*

As I turned over the situation in my mind, I could see the way the case would be presented. Having demonised me she was morally free to treat me as she wished. To cut off all ties with such a person was understandable, but to receive her back into the folds of the family would be an act of supreme kindness, highlighting her big-heartedness, condemning me further, aware that there would always be written into the subtext of our relationship the impression that I had behaved with such gross insensitivity and selfishness over my father's will. Of course, she'd never discuss the sorry business with Greg or me, for on the surface the whole matter had been brushed under the carpet and was to be left there. She was undoubtedly a clever lady my mother, I had to give her that.

I waited and waited and still the money didn't arrive. The days and weeks passed into a month until one day a postcard landed on the mat. It was from my mother announcing that she was visiting Susanna in Petersfield and could she 'pop in and see us on her way down'. I just felt angry; I hadn't yet received a penny of the inheritance I was entitled to. She had, as she said to Greg, left it a month, and it was all to be forgotten, and this 'forgetting' was to include the money I was due.

"What is she playing at?" I screamed in anger. "I thought you said she was going to send me the money and this is what I get, a good old V-sign. Look what a fool she is making of me. She might drop in! Golly, aren't we the lucky ones, what did I do to deserve this?" Bound up in this hard ball of anger were all the old jealousies and frustrations of my childhood. Dropping in to see me on her way to Petersfield! I was just incidental to her on her way to visit Susanna.

"Stop shouting at me. It's not my fault she is writing you cards like this. Do you think for one moment I am happy about the situation?"

"You told me she intended to send me the money. Where is it?"

"Jenny. Calm down please! Be reasonable. You know your mother doesn't rate me and I have no control over her actions."

"Well she is not coming here; I don't see why she should."

"Listen Jenny, I can arrange to go to Birmingham or Wales for the night, then your mother can stay here on her way to Petersfield and you can talk to her about her intentions, whether she means to give you the money or not. Try and talk to her about the Deed of Arrangement and explain that it was your father's wish that you should have that money.

"You must talk to her and try and build up your relationship with her. Don't you realise how traumatic your father's death has been for her? No one expected it and Jane must still be reeling from the shock; she is your mother after all."

Irritated, I asked, "What do you know about mother and daughter relationships, you aren't a daughter, you don't have any sisters and you've a mother who doesn't have any daughters or sisters for that matter, so what can you tell me about such relationships?"

"Maths is all about relationships. You think it's about numbers and computations, but it isn't, it's about relationships."

"What sort of relationships, marital, personal, interplanetary, sexual?"

"Quadratic equations. $ax^2+bx+c = 0$ is a quadratic equation. Formulas give you an answer, but what needs a formula and what doesn't; not all polynomials have a solution in the shape of a formula. Another interesting thing is credit card numbers. You can, with modern methods, work out a PIN number, but even with computers it could take years."

Sometimes his methods annoyed me so much; I could recognise the things he was good at, and, unfortunately, displacement activity was not one of them. How stupid did he think I was? I understood the point of this maths lesson all too well. A gauche attempt at changing the subject; he was trying to substitute my anger with a mathematical challenge. Well, he couldn't divert my mind that easily. I think psychologists believe anger can have a beneficial effect. I'd release some unfettered anger and see how my psyche benefited.

"This has got nothing to do with me and my mother. There aren't rules and conclusions, formulas and variables dealing with us, we're people, and I for one am not having her drop in on her way to see Susanna. It might be her formula for a solution but at this precise moment I am a polynomial with no solution, and she is going to have to try a bit harder if she genuinely wants one. And you say you'll go away for the night. Why don't you stay to discuss things with her, add to the numbers; you could be an interesting dimension perhaps? Complicate the computations," I barked angrily.

"It's easy to create a problem, the difficulty is solving it. Your mother might have created the problem," he said in exasperation, "but you've both got to sort things out, it's between the two of you. I think you should tell her she is welcome to stay, try and talk to her. Whatever you say, she wants to be friends with you, and she wants to see Alex. Once you and your mother are talking again then it'll be easier for me."

"How can you sit there and talk like that after everything we've been through in the last few months. I feel as though I've been to Hell and back and now you tell me to invite her to stay. I've to let her 'pop in on her way down to Susanna's' while you stay in a hotel somewhere. You always say you hate staying in hotels. Why can't you stay here if she comes?"

"No, I'm happy for you to invite her here; indeed I think you should, but I don't want to see her, can you not understand that?" He believed it was the right thing to do, he was trying to convince me for the best motives, still my gut feeling said no.

It was the casual offhand manner of the card, somehow setting the tone for the visit. It would be a breezy, casual evening with no mention of the furore of the past few months. If I was to mention the subject it would be stonewalled. I was behaving extremely badly over money. If that line didn't work she could fall back on the newly bereaved widow, pointedly leaving everything in the hands of people she could trust, and if I was to take offence it should be pointed out that Greg had resigned of his own free will. She was quite happy for him to stay on as executor if that was what he wanted, she had just called for a social visit. The last few months had been so awful I really don't want to discuss it Jenny. I could see it all, and having visited our house once, the door would be opened for her to call again.

"I know my mother, she will refuse to discuss anything about the will with me, and if I insist she will just start being unpleasant, or burst into tears and blame me for it all."

"As I've said before, she's a lot more likely to blame me than you."

"So that's why you won't stay if she comes here?"

"I've told you my reason, if you want to see her it's entirely up to you, I won't do anything to stop you seeing her."

"Well I don't see the point. She won't discuss the things that matter with me. I don't see why you should spend a night in a hotel when you would rather be here, and I don't like the casual way she's going to drop in on her way to Susanna's. I'll drop her a card and tell her it isn't convenient for her to stay, but next time I'm in Glasgow I'll let her know, and if she wants to she can see me then."

"Leave it a day or two and see how you feel."

"Why are you being so bloody reasonable?" I shouted, exasperated by his conviction that this was the correct way to proceed. Couldn't he see he was playing into her hands again?

"I feel it's wrong for you not to see your mother and I don't know what the solution is. I'm at my wit's end over this business. What can we do to put things right?" Greg pondered.

"Nothing. What can we do? Write back, and explain that I was ignorant of the correct etiquette when a recently bereaved mother announces she intends to double-cross me over my inheritance. Could she please inform me of the correct protocol, as unfortunately I am at a loss as to how to behave on this occasion?"

I sent a card, brief and to the point. It was not convenient for her to stay with us, and I might let her know next time I was in Glasgow visiting my in-laws; if she wanted to she could 'pop in and see me' then.

Chapter 11

A few weeks later another postcard lay on the carpet below the letter box, a scenic view of Loch Lomond with the evening sun sending a warm orange glow over the water. I looked at the picture for a minute before turning it over to see my mother's handwriting.

"Congratulations! I'm delighted to hear you're having another baby. I've started to knit a shawl for it. Mrs Johnstone has bought a flat in London and wants some curtains made. If you would like to give her a quote her number is …"

Angela must have told her the news.

The frustration feeding the anger erupted in a volcano. I lifted the fruit bowl off the kitchen table and hurled it at the floor, swiftly followed by my half full coffee cup. Greg moved quickly as I grabbed the plates on the table and they too were launched onto the floor. The noise was terrible as the china shattered with each renewed assault. The fragmented pieces ricocheted across the linoleum and rebounded against the skirting board leaving the floor like a sea of mosaic. The violence welled up inside me as I realised that the last few months of the wounding, the injuries and the heartache were to be swept aside and lost in a buzz of social niceties, overlaid by the impression of maternal concern. She wanted me to let her off the hook, keep my share of the inheritance and never discuss all the trouble over my father's will. Never to raise the matter again, while she was to enjoy all the appearance of a kind, concerned and no doubt generous parent, willing to forgive and forget.

"Why oh why did you let her off so lightly when she phoned you that time in the office? All you've done is cause trouble, it's all your fault that she thinks she can come here or drop us a card like this, because she believes you influence me enough to let her visit us," I screamed.

"I'm sure she knows you're quite capable of making up your own mind."

"I absolutely disagree with you," I shouted, "she thinks she has me over a barrel because of what you said."

"Stop it Jenny, for heaven's sake stop it. Can't you see I'm at my wit's end? I'm doing my best for you. I'm your husband, your best friend. Don't treat me like this." He was right; he didn't deserve this.

Feeling ashamed, I calmed down and spoke to him rationally. "What can I do to get her out of my life once and for all? She's making complete fools of us. I'm not bothered about the money any more. I just want to get shot of her forever."

"Are you sure?"

"Of course I'm sure," I said raising my voice again with irritation. "Why do you think I wrote that letter to her? I've told you, I want nothing more to do with her."

"If you're certain, I'll write to her now and put an end to this."

So I swept the floor while he drafted a letter.

Dear Mrs MacKenzie,

I do not think you have any conception of the heartache your deceit has caused to my wife and me. I simply do not understand what you are playing at. I have been very patient in this matter and had hoped that you would think upon what you were doing.

However, my patience is now totally exhausted. I can no longer tolerate the situation. My wife is under great emotional strain and I fear for her health and that of our unborn child.

I must therefore ask you to put an end to this situation once and for all. Do not contact us under any circumstances or under any pretext. If you do so, I shall seek an injunction through the courts.

Yours sincerely,

Greg Lorimer.

"I think this should convey the message," he said as I looked over his shoulder at what he had written.

"It does that all right, but will it have the desired effect? I know my mother well enough, she may want to keep my share of the inheritance, but she doesn't want to lose hold of me altogether; besides she enjoys her role as a grandmother," I said, "and martyr."

"At least now she knows she no longer has my support if she tries to contact you again."

I thought Greg was a little optimistic relying on a threatening letter to keep her at bay. Knowing my mother, I thought it would need more than this to deter her. What if she persisted in writing, trying to contact me, perhaps calling in with Susanna or Fay when visiting them? What would I do then? I must set about obtaining an injunction somehow. I couldn't have a repeat of the plate-throwing incident. I couldn't afford a repeat; a lot of our dinner service had disappeared in the bin that day.

The following day I had to attend the antenatal clinic, just a routine check with the midwife. Everyone called her Sister Mary and a more befitting name was impossible. The quite angelic serenity never left her face as she examined my bulbous midriff with her firm, warm hands. Then she turned those large dark, compassionate, eyes to my face and asked the usual question.

"Do you have any other problems Jenny?" This time I had. Looking up at her I told her everything; it was easy, as she listened quietly; she seemed to understand. I'd wrap the truth up in concern for my unborn child, and in that way disguise how feeble I was. Rounding off I asked her if she could help me obtain an injunction on medical grounds. After what had happened I thought the strain may be affecting the baby in some way, did she not agree?

"Babies are born in the most awful circumstances sometimes; in war-torn countries with bombs exploding and the mothers are under tremendous stress, but the babies aren't affected, so don't worry about the baby. It is understandably affecting you and it must be putting you and your husband under considerable strain, and your son as well. There is nothing I can do, only recommend that you talk to Dr. Sandy Black about it."

Rats! I'd been rumbled. She'd seen right through me and this wasn't the route I wanted to take. He wasn't a honey-tongued doctor with a tender bedside manner, he was a technician, a practitioner, brisk, efficient, quick to diagnose the strained muscle and recommend a course of physiotherapy. I could not think of him as a man interested in the psychological dimension of medicine. Besides, this was a Trust practice. Prioritisation was essential, and in the list of medical complaints I could only imagine that stress was a trivial matter, a pest for a doctor with more profound ailments to attend to.

Stress was a lifestyle problem; I'd just have to learn to control my feelings a bit more. Perhaps he would recommend a management strategy. With a little bit of will-power I could learn to change my attitude or habits; a simple self-care remedy would do. A bit more moral fibre was what was called for here. I could see it all so clearly. He was a doctor of the old school, not a man keen to encourage the discussion of emotional problems in his surgery.

"He'll be sympathetic, don't worry," she said, sensing my apprehension at the prospect of discussing this trouble with Dr. Black. "And, besides, I can't do anything practical to help you, but he can."

A few days later I was back in the clinic to retell the story to the man himself. Brevity was the keynote I decided, nothing mawkish or emotional; just tell him the facts in a straightforward manner.

"Sit down, Jenny," he said without looking up, as I entered his surgery. He continued keying data into a computer as I pulled the chair round, waiting for the cue to start my narrative.

"The midwife has written on your notes that you're having emotional problems since the death of your father, and that was almost a year ago from what I can gather." And here he released a sigh, which seemed to imply that a normal, balanced adult accepts this as part of life.

"Yes," I said feebly, realising my well-rehearsed speech was nothing more than a squalid tale of an argument over money. I shouldn't have pursued this course, but there was no backing out now. He detached himself from the keyboard and glided round to face me.

"And you are still upset by his death?" he queried, raising his eyebrows.

"'Yes I am, but that isn't the reason I'm here." I launched into an account of the disastrous outcome of my father's will. The worrying time Rory and my mother had had immediately following my father's death and their relief when Greg discovered how a Deed of Arrangement could solve the financial crisis. How happy I'd been for a short while, believing that, at last, Greg would be accepted into the family, and through their gratitude for Greg my standing in the family would be confirmed. My mother and I would enjoy a close relationship. How it had all gone so terribly wrong and how I just wanted nothing to do with any of my family now. He listened intently, leaning back in the chair, his fingers linked over his chest as the elbows rested on the arms of the chair. I concluded with my explanation for wanting to secure an injunction against my mother.

"Jenny, that is an appalling story. I know nothing about injunctions, but I advise you very strongly to have crisis counselling."

"Counselling?" I repeated suspiciously, thinking of the stigma attached. Therapy for dysfunctional beings.

"Yes. Counselling," he confirmed. "It won't do you any harm and I think it will help you. We have a trained counsellor, who specialises in crisis counselling. She comes here every Thursday and I would like you to discuss everything with her."

"Oh," I said as I sank back in the chair. I was baffled. This concern; it wasn't what I had expected.

"Your future is with Greg and your children; you don't need to have anything to do with a mother that behaves like that towards you. I didn't have a good relationship with my mother but she would never have treated me like that. Crisis counselling is for cases like this. I will refer you to the counsellor and she will contact you as soon as she has a space."

"It sounds like one step from the psychiatrist's chair."

"Psychiatrists help patients with a mental illness. This isn't the case here. You have a very unpleasant problem which is not of your making, and hopefully talking to Pip will help you come to terms with it."

Chapter 12

Dear Jenny,

As you know, one of the assets of your father's estate was his entitlement to receive half of the residue of the estate of his late Aunt, Miss M. D. MacKenzie. We managed to obtain payment of the final balance due in that respect only very recently. The fact of that payment having been received has allowed your mother to assess her own financial position with more accuracy than was possible until now. I have checked through all the relevant figures with your mother, including the very considerable payments which she made from her own funds to settle liabilities which were truly due from your father's estate. As you will appreciate, your mother has not received, and will not receive, any liquid funds from your father's estate; in fact, she has had to provide funds to the estate to cover the amount by which the sum of the tax bills and the payments made to the family exceeded the liquid funds which were available for uplifting from the bank, building society, et cetera.

Allowing for all of these factors, your mother is happy to make a gift to you of £17,000; and she is making a gift of the same amount to Henry and to each of your sisters, but not to Rory.

Your mother has asked me to write to you and to your sisters and to Henry on her behalf about this and so I am now happy to enclose her cheque in your favour for £17,000.

For reasons of potential tax, et cetera, it is important that we have a clear record of these payments. I therefore enclose a receipt and shall be grateful if you will sign that and if you will return it to me in the envelope provided.
With kind regards.

Yours sincerely,

Peter.

The cheque fell to the floor as I read the letter. Greg picked it up and looked at it.

"At last!" he exclaimed.

"I don't want it; it's been the cause of so much trouble," I uttered.

"Why ever not?" said Greg incredulously. "After all, it's what your father wanted you to have, it's rightfully yours, and you can't just give it up like that, especially when you consider what we've been through for it."

"I suppose you are right, but at the moment it gives me no pleasure. If I cash it I have no reason not to see my mother again, and the way I feel at the moment, I'd rather not see my mother than have the money."

"That's not how I see it. As far as I am concerned they are two separate issues. You have the money, which is rightfully yours, and whether you see your mother or not is a different issue. You can now decide whether or not you see your mother again. The first thing you do is go down to the town and bank it. Do you hear me?"

"I have my appointment to see the counsellor tomorrow, because I wasn't getting my inheritance, and now it's come through."

"Think rationally, Jenny. You've been referred to the counsellor because of the emotional state you are in over the way your mother's treated you regarding your inheritance, and that hasn't changed. Go and see this lady tomorrow. As you say, you have your appointment and it's too late to give the appointment to someone else."

I banked the cheque that day and the following afternoon, armed with dark glasses and paper hankies for the likely event of me crying, I kept my appointment with Pip Barker.

She sat, plump and wholesome like a well risen cake, listening. Her arms crossed in front of her ample bosom as they all perched comfortably on the desk in front of her, and I sat and retold the doleful story I had told Dr. Black less than two weeks ago. There was one difference; I'd received my inheritance yesterday and now I felt like a fraud. She asked me questions. Was I the eldest child? What were my mother's relations like with her other children? Did my parents get on well? Had I been to boarding school? Had my mother been to boarding school? Pip could sympathise with me, she said. She was from Perth; her relationship with her mother had been an unhappy one.

"If I take you on as a patient, what do you expect from counselling?"

"Help to get over the traumas of the last six months and coming to terms with never seeing my family again."

She nodded her head in approval and made an appointment for the next week, and this would be a regular slot for me fortnightly for as long as I needed it. So the counselling began. Before every appointment I'd wonder what else there was to talk about, then with her professional, slightly schoolmarmish manner she'd ask a leading question, bouncing me into some theme. It seems, looking back on it, that we'd cover a different topic each week, and as I talked she'd look at me intently, as though fascinated by what I had to say. Oh, the indulgence of counselling! I sat and talked about myself for one whole hour as Pip sat opposite and grunted in an interested fashion, smiled in a motherly fashion, and occasionally, at each meeting, jotted down a note or two.

With professional interest she prodded and pressed, enquired and commiserated, not unlike the midwife I suppose, only with her it was my psyche she was trying to push in the right direction, not the baby in my tummy. Trying to gauge the relationships, the background of the relationships, positions in the family, the causes of the tensions.

Unearthing memories kept buried for years, I told her things I had never told a soul. Was she genuinely interested? I don't know. Was it relevant? I don't know, but I told her anyway. If I wanted the counselling to be of use I must be honest and tell her everything.

She seemed to like stories; I suppose they give a good picture. I told her of the tenant, Mr Munroe, who'd rented the gamekeeper's cottage when it was still habitable, just. He was a hairy, unkempt-looking young man, who said he wanted to stay there for the views. My parents were glad of the extra money,. Although they were surprised anyone wanted to live in the house.

Mum reckoned he was probably a drop-out, judging by his hair and clothes. We, the children, were not to talk to him or go near the house. A couple of weeks into the let, Mum realised his true reason for renting the house. How stupid of her not to have realised when it was so obvious. He was a drug dealer. He'd drive off to Glasgow at midday, sometimes later, and not return until the early hours of the morning. The best course of action was to inform the police the next time she went past the police station. Before she had an opportunity to become an informer, she read an article in the Glasgow Herald about a documentary being made about 'The changing face of Glasgow' by a brilliant young film producer. It was our tenant Mr Munroe. The next week when he paid the rent, she invited him for tea.

Then I told Pip the story of the diary. How Ursula and her brood were enjoying a Sunday lunch with us, and in a lull in the conversation my mother reached down into her handbag and produced, of all things, my diary. My kind grandmother, in an attempt to improve my spelling skills, had given it to me at New Year and suggested I write in it, perhaps describing the type of day I'd had or what I had done. So religiously, every day for a couple of months, I wrote of the events in my life, until the diary mysteriously disappeared. Now I discovered my mother had requisitioned it for her purposes. To amuse friends and family with my early writings.

"I went to skool," she read out. "Skool spelt s-k-o-o-l. And the next day we have 'I went to skool', and look here we have another 'I went to skool'. And here it becomes interesting," she laughed, "I did well in a speling test at skool'. Spelling spelt s-p-e-l-i-n-g."

"And school?" enquired Ursula.

"We always spell school s-k-o-o-l." My mother spluttered with laughter.

My siblings and cousins, caught up in the general hilarity, laughed along with the adults, hardly understanding the joke, but understanding this was the correct thing to do. My father sat, rigid with cold anger at the end of the table.

"Stop this at once Jane," he said.

She couldn't, there were more gems she had to share with her audience.

"I must read you this page; Gail Jones thought this was hysterical."

How awful, she'd read it to her friend. I squirmed back in my seat, bracing myself for the next bout of humiliation. Thankfully, my father intervened, raising his voice.

"Put that away now." This time she responded. The diary was returned to the handbag and that was the last I saw of it.

Pip's family had been cruel to her as well; it was worse for her, she told me, as she was an only child. She also had been packed off to boarding school at a young age. As the weeks passed I discovered Pip would divulge unsolicited confidences with me, as a sort of bonding act. I understood the point of her sharing these selected confidences. I could confide in her because of our shared experiences; we could empathise together, so I did.

I explained how the doctors had misdiagnosed the cause of my asthma, resulting in my mother's heartless management of the illness, aided and abetted by Ursula. Pip wanted to know more about my aunt, but then lots of people did. I told her how Ursula had initially become involved in politics while at University. My grandparents first became aware just how involved one morning when buying the Scotsman newspaper. Her face was blazoned across the front page, leading a demonstration. There was no disguising the fact that it was their daughter; her name stood out in bold print.

In her early student years she was constantly at loggerheads with Euan Stone, a fellow law student and president of the student's union. On the occasional weekends, or the university holidays, when she returned to her parents' house for a square meal, she'd complain and grumble about this little runt of a man, a crackpot imbecile, too stupid and unprincipled to be capable of making the right decision about anything.

When she announced that she intended to live with Euan ('in sin' as the term was then) Ann and Douglas were genuinely surprised. Ursula had ended up sitting next to him at a University dinner. Euan had arrived late at the reception and had the choice of sitting next to Ursula or the Vice Chancellor. Hadn't she always said he couldn't make the right decision?

After university she qualified as a solicitor and was the main breadwinner for several years as Euan pursued his political ambitions. She was more radical than Euan, more outspoken. He was a politician, charismatic, an impressive orator and a witty debater, more pragmatic than his partner and extremely good-looking. I've noticed handsome men often marry very plain women. Is it because they are also vain and want all the attention themselves or because being attractive to the opposite sex, they've experienced women throwing themselves at their feet and have decided not to have a wife subjected to the same temptations, in reverse, so to speak? Despite the contrast in their appearances, they were intellectually and politically well matched, both being fervent nationalists. One felt they were destined never to be more than opposition politicians. Ursula's non-conformist personality was always eager to take a rebellious stand in search of a purpose. Feeling tremendous empathy for the underdog, she revelled in fighting the worthy cause. Conscious of the value of her opinions and her self-righteous moral superiority, she attached inordinate importance to herself. Her superiority was worn like a badge, displayed conspicuously with a sort of proud defiance. *I am the champion of an admirable, but unpopular cause, which could sink without trace if not for my committed zeal.* Her mission was to change the structure of society. She was 'the public just need educating' variety of politician. Once she'd explained to the less enlightened and shaped their thoughts, they would understand. Society had a lot to learn from her. There wasn't a hint of modesty about the woman.

Euan, a public figure as a political commentator and a newspaper columnist, became a Member of Parliament in his mid-twenties. Now married to a celebrity, her popularity within the family soared. Many of them treated her with added deference. They paid greater attention when she spoke. Fuelled by their interest she spoke even more, but worse, she spoke well and knew it. Delighting in the sound of her own voice, she'd broadcast her views. She must be listened to. It was imperative.

She liked to be taken seriously, and she was, by her sister anyway.

Visiting us, she would give voice to the issues that passionately concerned her. We had no option but to listen, as she lectured about such wide-ranging issues as anti-apartheid, abortion, children's rights, or an independent parliament for Scotland. These social injustices were matters on the fringes of the political agenda of the time, but she would redress the balance. She cared enormously about humanity; it was flawed individuals, deficient personalities she had no time for. She never hesitated to demonstrate to those around her the fact that I was such a person.

Pip tried to persuade me to see Ursula in a different light, a principled woman who stuck to her guns. Perhaps I thought Ursula was misguided, but she was basically a well-meaning person, Pip reasoned. What a fool. You'd think a counsellor would have enough savvy not to be conned like everyone else by Ursula's public persona. She was an unmitigated pain.

I told her of the treacle scones. Every year before Christmas the W.I. ladies of Balcruen held a bring-and-buy sale in the village hall. One year my mother took along some treacle scones for the cake stall. I'll give my mother her due; she made delicious scones, but these were the best. Being treacle-flavoured, however, they did look a rather strange colour, perhaps not appetising to someone who had never tasted them. At the end of the sale, the only item left sitting on the cake stall were my mother's treacle scones. My mother, realising they might well end up in the pig bin if she didn't retrieve them, approached Mrs Campbell, the lady who had been selling cakes all afternoon and announced that she would like to buy the remaining scones. Mrs Campbell, believing my mother to be acting on a charitable impulse, salvaging the remnants of her stall, advised her kindly.

"I wouldn't buy those if I was you Mrs Mackenzie, they don't look very good."

I don't know what most people would have done in that situation, but my mother answered her unabashed.

"Well, my children think they are delicious. I know they'll all be eaten up tonight."

There was a moment's hesitation while the penny dropped and before the poor woman managed to utter, "Oh! I'm so sorry Mrs MacKenzie, I had no idea," as she wrapped the offending articles in a brown paper bag. Her head was bent down as the colour rose to her cheeks; she was mortified at the clanger she had just dropped.

I told Pip how the one member of my family who had genuinely liked me, Aunt Barbara, had been incarcerated in a psychiatric hospital for a large part of her adult life.

"What was the worst thing that happened to you as a child?" she asked one day.

I blushed and looked away. Even now, over twenty years after the event, a wave of shame came over me. It wasn't so much that I had run away from home, lots of children do that, it was the reason. Why should I still find it distressing after all this time? Surely a mature adult would have learnt to overcome the humiliation, possibly to laugh at the whole incident. I weighed it up painfully. I'd tell her 'Warts and all'.

"I ran away from home when I was fifteen," I answered slowly, and without waiting for the predictable 'Why?' I launched into the explanation. "For some reason my mother was anxious for me to become a Queen's Guide. I suppose she thought I wasn't much good at anything else; at least I could be a Queen's Guide. I hated the Guides; the French teacher from school ran it. I didn't like her. I suppose I was a nightmare pupil and she did not pretend to like me. Every girl from my year was a sixer. That meant they were in charge of their group. In fact, there were some girls from the year below me that were sixers. My own sixer was almost a year younger than me. I felt I was no more than a figure of fun. At times the sixers would be called out for meetings with the Guide Leader and I tried to make light of the situation, the only one of my age left behind, the only year four girl not to have made the grade. It was awful. I had asked my mother if I could stop going to Guides, but she wasn't having any of it. It was 'character building', she said, and I needed lots of that.

"It must have been about October; my mother asked me at table when I was going to become a Queen's Guide. It was a Friday. I'd come home after Guides and I was having a late tea with my parents and my sister Elizabeth. I didn't need to make enquiries to ask if I could become a Queen's Guide. I knew the answer already.

"I don't think Miss Clark will let me be a Queen's Guide," I mumbled.

"Why on earth not?" my mother demanded to know.

"I just don't think she will," I replied timidly.

"We'll see about that," she said angrily, pushing back her chair and heading for the phone.

"I don't know what my mother said to Miss Clark, but what she said to my mother haunts me to this day. When my mother returned she was in a rage shouting at me hysterically.

'Miss Clark says not one teacher has a good word to say for you. Not one teacher has a good word to say for you'. I remember her repeating the sentences and wondering if Miss Clark had as well. 'You are a thoroughly unpleasant child, a thoroughly unpleasant child'.

I think it was the sight of my father sitting at the table rigid with disappointment and unable to say a word that upset me most. I looked at him, hoping for some sign of kindness, but there was only anger and all of it targeted at me, as my mother ranted on. Eventually, I left the table in tears and went to my bedroom.

I wrote a note to my parents, I can't remember what I wrote, but it was to the effect that I never wanted to see them again. I left it on my bed, changed my clothes and headed for the woods. I spent the night in the woods, thinking I would hitch-hike down to London the next day in a lorry. Somehow I managed to sleep in the woods for I can remember waking up feeling incredibly cold and stiff, and shortly after that I heard people shouting my name. Although I was fifteen, I was a very young-looking fifteen, I looked more like thirteen and I thought no lorry driver would pick me up. I suppose also, in the cold light of day, I got cold feet at the prospect of going to London. I spent the day in the woods and a second night and then returned to my bed in the early hours of the morning."

"What happened then?"

"I was interviewed by the police and a woman in plain clothes, who I took to be a social worker. She kept asking me if I was upset because I didn't have a boyfriend. I seem to remember I had told the girls at school I had one, when I didn't. There was no way they could contradict me as I lived so far away from them; they had no idea what I did in the evenings or weekends. I kept telling the social worker I couldn't care less if I had a boyfriend or not."

"How did you feel about that?"

"I was very upset about not having a boyfriend, but I wasn't going to tell her that."

"Did you go back to the school?"

"Yes, I went back for almost two more years."

She shook her head in disbelief. "Did you have counselling?"

This time I looked in disbelief. Counselling? Over twenty years ago in Scotland? It was unheard of. Even now it would probably be regarded as something fashionably wacky for those nutters with more money than sense. Where had she been? "No," I answered. "But I did become a Queen's Guide a few months after that," I told her, thinking it might be relevant. She shook her head in more disbelief.

"Perhaps I did have counselling of sorts. I saw the headmistress and she told me what a terrible weekend Miss Clark had had. The headmistress had spent her Sunday morning at the Hydro looking for Miss Clark, who was attending a conference for Guide leaders. Miss Clark had turned white when the headmistress appeared at the conference. Why did I think that was? She was probably embarrassed to see you there. No, I was to stop being facetious. She was very worried about me. I was left in no doubt as to the trouble I had caused my parents, the teachers, the police, my whole family. Everyone was being very kind to me and I was never to do anything like that again."

"Tell me how you got on at that school generally."

"Not very well. I think by this time my parents were really feeling the pinch financially. I'm sure if they could have afforded to, they would have kept me at a boarding-school. As it was I became a day-girl at the nearest private school to my parents' farm, a school roughly twenty miles away.

"I never got on particularly well at the secondary school, being a day-girl at a predominantly boarding school. We were called 'the day bugs' by the boarders; they found the bed bugs in the beds and the day bugs in the day, both irritating vermin and difficult to get rid of."

"That upset you."

"It was nothing personal. It was after the absconding incident when things got nasty. The teachers closed ranks behind Miss Clark."

"In what way?"

"There were nearly always a couple of rows of desks down one side of the classroom which weren't occupied. Several of the teachers, Miss Clark included, would insist I sat in the corner next to the back wall on my own. I was constantly excluded from outings or events."

"You felt ostracised?"

"More like a clay pigeon. The teachers would catapult me into the air for anyone to take a pot shot at."

"Can you explain what you mean?"

"I felt they were always trying to make me look stupid. If I mispronounced a word or gave the wrong answer, they'd make a point of ridiculing me in front of the whole class and, in response, there'd be ripples of sycophantic laughter from other pupils. I pretended I couldn't care less, but I hated being the butt of the teachers' jibes and sarcasm.

My attitude degenerated into one of virtual anarchy. I became industriously idle and refused do my homework. To avoid getting into trouble one day I bunked off school, and wandered around Bridge of Allan. Nothing was said; so I started skipping school regularly and in this way everyone was happy. The headmistress was happy to take the fees off my parents. My parents believed paying for an education meant I was being given one and were kept in blissful ignorance. The teachers, having one less difficult pupil in the classroom, couldn't care less and neither could I. One day at lunchtime I bumped into a friend and she told me there had been a fire drill and as I couldn't be accounted for when the register was taken, the teacher announced, to everyone's amusement, that I had been burnt. Two years later, locked into a nurses training which I hated, I was to bitterly regret bunking off and still do to this day."

"Was there no one you could speak to? How about your grandmother?"

"I know she spoke to my mother about how unhappy I was, but my mother saw the situation as a battle of wills and I wasn't going to win, or in other words, change schools.

"With my poor academic achievements, I decided the best career for me was nursing. My mother had made it clear she wanted me off her hands financially and nursing answered all my requirements, an acceptable career for a non academic. I'd be financially independent and at the end of three years the world would be my oyster, or so I was told."

"So what happened?"

"The oyster is still waiting for me."

"You didn't finish your training?"

"I almost didn't. After about eighteen months I decided I'd had enough of anti-social hours, which dictated my life, while other young people seemed to be having a whale of a time. I went home on one of my days off and told my parents I was giving up nursing. They were furious. What a waste of all the training I'd had; they'd be so disappointed in me if I left, and had I thought about what I'd do with no qualifications to my name. Who'd want to employ a dropout nurse? I think it was fear that kept me nursing, fear that what they said was true. What else could I do? So not having the nerve to leave I qualified as a nurse, and then left to become a waitress at Aviemore."

"How did your parents take it?"

"They were furious. 'Had I thought about how it would affect my prospects?' they asked. I suppose they thought once I'd qualified I'd carry on nursing, and with a bit of luck I might just marry a doctor. However, I refused to spend the rest of my life locked into a job I didn't like. With hindsight I'm glad they convinced me to finish my training, but giving up nursing was the best thing I did.

"After the stint as a waitress I spent the summer backpacking round Europe and in the autumn I returned to London penniless. I was grateful then that my parents had persuaded me to complete my nurse's training because I was able to walk straight into a job at Guys Hospital. It wasn't the most desirable position, but I was desperate to restock my depleted bank balance and they were having trouble finding a nurse to work in the V.D. clinic."

"How did you like going back to nursing?"

"This time I enjoyed it, away from all the stiff starchiness of the Edinburgh medical scene, where we'd been instructed to stand up if a doctor came into the room and to treat them with great respect. The casual informality of the V.D. clinic was a pleasant relief and I look back on that time as the happiest period of my nursing career."

"Because of the informality?"

"Yes partly. I had to work along side the largest, jolliest nurse I'd ever come across called Abigail Mundugfufu. On my first day she informed me, through her thick Malawi accent, I could either call her Abigail or Mrs Mundugfufu but never Fufu, so like everyone else on the department I called her Fufu."

"What did your parents think about you working in a V.D. clinic?"

"I don't think I ever told them and they never asked. They were just thankful I was back on the tracks, as they saw it. They knew that I was working in outpatients at Guys Hospital, a renowned medical establishment with a prestigious medical school and presumably this upped my chances of marrying a doctor. They seemed relieved.

"After nine months I began to be bored with the work. I wanted a complete change. I couldn't see myself as a career nurse. One lunchtime I dropped into a careers advice centre aimed at school leavers, not disaffected nurses. However, they listened to me. I had a good idea of what I wanted to do. I wanted to make soft furnishings. It probably sounds a pretty strange thing to want to do, but I'd discovered, working in outpatients, that I liked running my own show. In outpatients the nurse was responsible for running her clinic; no one interfered, so long as things went smoothly. I thought if I made soft furnishings I would be responsible for the outcome. I'd always enjoyed sewing and been reasonably good at it. It was a skill my grandmother had taught me, so why not try and make a career out of something I enjoyed?

"The careers adviser arranged an interview for me the next week at London College of Furniture. There was a day release course in soft furnishing, exactly the sort of thing I wanted. He drew me a map of how to get there and told me what explanation to give about wanting to quit nursing.

"At the college I explained everything to the lecturer who interviewed me.

"'You don't want to do that course, it's full of boring middle-aged ladies,' he advised me. 'There's one place left on the interior design course. You'd find it very interesting and it would be much more suitable for you.'

"As I'd worked full time for more than three years I was entitled to a full grant. An interior designer sounded terribly grand, so I thought I'd give it a go. My mother was furious when I told her.

'Just like you were at school,' I remember her screaming, 'you can't stick anything can you?' After spending three agreeable years at college, I realised that to succeed in the interior design world one had to be tough, well connected and very good. Not being any of these, I decided to work in a small soft furnishing workshop where I could learn what I had originally wanted to. Ironically, I was worse off working than I had been on a student grant, so I started to do work on my own at weekends. Fairly soon after that I took the plunge and became self-employed. I thought I'd do this for a couple of years and then progress on to something else. That was fifteen years ago."

Pip was interested in knowing how I'd met Greg. I told her how I'd been working in Scotland, making furnishings for a hotel and Rose asked me if I wanted to go to a disco with her. I wasn't very keen, but she persuaded me to go along with her."

"Why didn't you want to go?"

"I'm not very good at dancing or talking to people I've never met before and I suppose I thought it wasn't the way to meet a nice man. Some cruel friends tell me I was quite right there."

"So you met him at a disco."

131

"Sort of. I met his friend at a disco and he asked me out for a drink that Tuesday. I went along to the pub, half expecting him not to be there, and he wasn't; Greg was there instead. I recognised him from the disco and he explained how Peter had had to attend a police identity parade and, as he hadn't taken my telephone number, he couldn't contact me. He had asked Greg if he could meet me in the pub to explain his non-appearance."

"Did you go out with Peter?"

"Yes, a couple of times, but I preferred Greg."

"What made you like Greg?"

"I suppose, with us, it's a case of opposites attracting. He's a natural academic. He's always found maths fascinating and I gather he shone at most subjects at school, except art. Art was always my favourite subject and I just could not get my brain round maths. He always knew he wanted to be a mathematician, and I'm still wondering what I'm going to do when I grow up. He's cautious in everything he does and I'm forever opening my mouth before my brain's engaged and saying the wrong thing."

Pip told me she understood what it was like being married to a clever man; her husband had a first-class honours degree from Cambridge University.

"Shortly after we married, Greg landed a job in the city and we moved to an area of Islington where most of the houses had seen better days, although the estate agent assured us the area was on the up and this proved to be true. We had neighbours of all sorts. There were the established residents, tailors, builders, taxi drivers who'd lived in the area all their lives, and then there were the newcomers who moved there for the convenience of the city. The yuppies they called us, although I never felt like a yuppie myself.

I remember our next-door neighbour, one of the original residents, telling me with pride that she'd even had lawyers in her house. I didn't tell her it was nothing to boast about. We lived there for seven years until Greg's work took him to Reading."

At the end of my narrative Pip suggested that, before our next meeting, I should think about my mother, the sort of person she is, and try to analyse why she should have such negative feelings towards me.

I'd always thought my asthma was the cause of our fraught relationship, and she was imposing a penance on me, which I couldn't shake off. Perhaps I had been missing something? I'd told Pip of her strange childhood. Conceived in Ghana. Perhaps that wasn't so strange, since a lot of West Africa was colonised by the British, but her early life was by most people's standards unusual. Could that have affected her in some way? Or I wondered if the reason was genetic and my mother had inherited this characteristic from her father, whose meanness, notorious throughout the family, had been put down to his impoverished childhood, growing up in a tenement flat with a widowed mother forced to work. My father had refused to get involved with him in any sort of business or financial transaction and, thinking about it now, I don't know if he'd ever really trusted my mother with money. It could be a congenital defect.

"Possibly it was because I wasn't a boy. Although Susanna is her favourite, I think she would have liked more sons. As recently as our ill-fated holiday in St Andrews, she had informed me what a comfort sons are when a woman is widowed, as I'd probably find out. I did refrain from saying, 'I couldn't wait', and put the tactless remark down to her strange behaviour that week. Even so, the remark did not altogether surprise me. I have heard of mothers who, subconsciously, never stop blaming their first child for the dramatic change in their lives after the infant is born. However, I still think the reason was my asthma."

"No, I don't think it has anything to do with your asthma. I think it's because your mother is a bully and what you experienced at her hands is child abuse."

I gasped in surprise. The term was too strong, too emotive, an overreaction. My mother being categorised as a child abuser, it was absurd. Child abusers are perverts who commit unimaginable atrocities. In prison they have to be separated from other prisoners for their own protection. On the Richter scale of child abuse, what my mother did would barely register. Children were removed from their families for child abuse; there was never any question of that happening to me. She'd misunderstood.

"She doesn't like you, she never has and she will always blame you for everything," Pip continued as though I hadn't got the point. "She just doesn't like you."

I'd already gathered Pip wasn't hidebound by the conventional notion that mothers loved their children whatever, but I wasn't prepared for this ruthless form of feedback. I had expected, if not a more elaborate explanation, certainly a slightly less brutal one.

"Why not?" I asked.

"Because you are the weakest of her children and you won't stand up to her."

"What do you mean by weakest?" I queried, preparing myself for the next forthright answer; she certainly didn't intend to delude me. How much more of this could I take?

"Easily upset, anxious to please, willing to forgive," she recited textbook fashion as I slumped back in the chair. Anxious to please, willing to forgive, were those signs of weakness I wondered?

"I wouldn't say I'd been exactly 'anxious to please' or 'willing to forgive' this time," I pointed out rationally.

"You won't stand up to her; you aren't prepared to discuss the matter with her. Are you?"

"She won't discuss it with me," I argued.

"She might not want to discuss it with you, but you haven't really tried to discuss it with her, have you?" she continued. "You must change, learn to stand up to her, not let her push you around."

"I can't dramatically change the way I am."

"You can if you want to. It's not so difficult to stand up to her."

"How? You don't know my mother."

"No, but I know you and I don't think you are good at arguing your point. You must discuss it with her. You've had opportunities to talk to her and you don't. You mustn't let her bully you. It's as though you are hiding behind a parapet, and every now and then you peep over the top, don't like what you see and dive down again for cover. Do you think that is an accurate description?" she enquired, pleased with her analogy.

I gave a wry smile in acknowledgement.

"I've never thought of her as a bully before, it seems a horrible thing to say about one's mother. So if I'm not around she will probably start bullying one of the others."

"I don't think that is the answer. I think you are the sort of person who needs a family." *Too weak to cope without, was that the implication? I wasn't going to ask.*

"When I came here the first time you asked me what I expected from counselling and I remember telling you: 'Coming to terms with not seeing my family again'. Now you are telling me I should see them."

"Yes I think you should. You would rather be on friendly terms with your mother than not, wouldn't you?" She looked at me for a moment as I deciphered this logic.

All the time I'd spent divulging grudges, misdeeds of my past, boosted and encouraged by her professional, somehow detached, yet curious and attentive grunts and nods. I believed she was backing me, supporting me as she coaxed me along, taking for granted that all this information, this unhappy history, would be put to good use as a vindication for the final severance of all family ties, frail though the ties may be. I'd arrived today convinced that, with the knowledge I had given her, she would provide the formula I needed for the emotional break. Now she was advising me to take a one hundred and eighty-degree change of direction. I felt I'd been completely misled. At what point had she decided I should have a reconciliation with my mother? Perhaps it had been her intention all along.

I had come looking for the courage to make the final break. Now she was telling me that was the cowardly way. The flip side was to confront my mother, stand up to her and be bold.

"I didn't get on at all well with my mother, as I've told you," she said, breaking the silence. "But then I learnt to stand up to her and, after that, we had a much better relationship. She learnt to respect me, and that is what you've got to do."

Little Goody Two Shoes, I thought. *You've had your child abuse, done your counselling course. Been there, done that. Aren't you wonderful the way you've coped? I too could be like you.*

What I did say was, "You were an only child; I've got five brothers and sisters to compete with."

"It's better for you, psychologically, to see your mother and to stand up to her."

"I don't know how I can stand up to her."

"Don't worry, if nothing else she'll want to see her grandchildren. I'm a grandmother and I know how important it is to see my grandchildren."

"I've to see my mother so she can see her grandchildren?"

"That isn't what I am saying. I wouldn't do anything to jeopardise seeing my grandchildren and your mother won't be so different. I suspect you're not very good at having rational discussions or arguments. You've to learn to be polite but firm. You must toughen up and learn not to let her upset you."

"It's the way I am. I know I am oversensitive. Even if I was tougher I can't see myself standing up to her. She can be very 'strong', I'd call it aggressive, and I can't cope with it. She always goes for the jugular and upsets me every time."

"Yes, I know she does, but you've not to let her; there is no reason to. You have a successful marriage, a wonderful son, your own business."

"It's only making loose covers and curtains."

"Don't put yourself down. Do you think she could do that?"

"I honestly don't know. It doesn't take a lot of intelligence."

"It takes a certain amount of cleverness to get it up and running, keep it going, deal with all the book keeping, ordering the correct quantities of fabric, satisfying the customers and you've got a family as well."

"Greg helps me a lot."

"You've a very supportive husband; you've a lot to look forward to. You spend your time thinking about what your mother has done, don't you?"

"Yes," I agreed.

"Well don't, you're giving her power over you. Do you think she thinks about you much? I shouldn't think she does. She has lots of interests you tell me, curling, gardening, the farm, her other children, a wide circle of friends and relatives."

"I'm sure she enjoys criticizing me in front of them, telling them what a frightful daughter I am."

"People aren't stupid; they make up their own minds."

"My family certainly agree with her."

"How do you know?"

"Not one of them sent me a Christmas card last year."

"Did you send any of them a Christmas card?"

"No, but you'd have thought one of them might have."

"It's over twenty years since you lived there. You have to go back and act as an adult in front of them; you are every bit as good as they are. Don't let them push you around. You might be surprised at the reaction you get. Remember she is an old woman now, she has no hold over you, and you're a free agent."

My expectation of counselling was that it would help to prevent depression. At that moment it appeared to be aimed in the opposite direction. I came away feeling at a low ebb, my self-esteem shattered. Possibly, things had to get worse before they got better. Perhaps Pip understood something about my personality that Greg and Dr. Black and I didn't. I'd persevere; she was probably right.

I was to be desensitised. Pip would help me. She would spend the next few sessions explaining to me how to stand up to my mother's bullying, how to ignore her when she upset me.

Chapter 13

A few days later Ba called. I hadn't heard from her for months. All contact with her had stopped abruptly after the holiday in St Andrews. My mother would win the propaganda war with Ba, I knew without doubt, for Ba still regarded me as a child and adults must act in concert against wayward children. Her profession as a teacher, educating the young ladies of the Edinburgh middle classes in a private school (naturally), had taught her that. I knew from her eyes the case against me was already hopelessly prejudiced.

"Hello dear, it's Ba." Ba was the youngest of four girls born within five years of each other in India to a handsome Edinburgh lady, married to a military doctor many years her senior. Her father retired from the medical service while Ba was still an infant, but the name the Indian nurse bestowed on her was to remain all her life.

"I've just been talking to your mother dear, and she's terribly upset at not having any contact with you."

"I'm upset about the situation as well."

"I don't see what the problem is; you've got the money you wanted."

"It isn't the money that's the problem, it's the way she's treated me."

"I know you and Mummy have always had a very difficult relationship, but she doesn't treat you any differently from any of the others."

"Yes she does, and she always has."

"Don't be ridiculous. Your poor father and grandfather must be turning in their graves at what is happening."

Taking a deep breath I started talking to her calmly. But within no time my voice rose and quavered.

"You're like Mummy, you're blaming me for everything. It's just like my counsellor said; I'd always be blamed for everything."

"Who's this counsellor? Is he a doctor or something? If he doesn't know your mother how can he make this ludicrous statement?"

Words came flooding out, awkward, ill thought out, and erratic utterances in a stream of emotional hysteria. Not what I'd intended. I searched frantically for those carefully constructed sentences that I'd rehearsed with Pip. Those words had vanished, evaporated. Instead I garbled half-sentences. I knew I was havering, making a fool of myself. I cried, furious with myself, I mentioned the threat of an injunction.

"It's all very confusing dear; Mummy hasn't said anything about an injunction to me. I'd be interested to know what it's all about."

"Shouldn't you have found out before you phoned me?" I said with an edge in my voice that wasn't meant to be there.

"I only want to pour oil on troubled waters." she retorted defensively.

"I'll send you the correspondence and then you'll understand everything."

Dear Ba,

In our last telephone conversation you expressed an interest in seeing the correspondence. The background is that in St Andrews, Mummy gave Greg the clear impression that she was not going to carry out Daddy's wishes. Greg then wrote to Peter Wright to resign as executor on the grounds that Daddy's wishes were not being carried out. No one wrote to Greg to say there had been a misunderstanding and Greg resigned.

Peter Wright's letter was far from clear and I wrote to Mummy to clarify the point. Instead of saying that she was going to carry out Daddy's wishes, Rory wrote to me saying that all future correspondence would be with Peter Wright. This was a disastrous response. The fact that neither Mummy nor Rory would give a straight answer to a simple question shows that at that stage Mummy did not intend to carry out Daddy's wishes.

If she had intended to carry out Daddy's wishes, why did she not say so and put an end to the turmoil? Since Mummy had passed the letter to the lawyers I thought the lawyer's response was going to be that my mother did not want to see me again. I decided to pre-empt this by telling her first.

I would like a reconciliation with Mummy, but cannot accept that we were responsible for the trouble. I don't think Mummy did this out of self-interest. I believe that others close to her influenced her, but only she can say why she behaved the way she did. I hope this letter explains the situation to you.

I hope you enjoy your Christmas break. We are staying in Henley for Christmas. Alex is getting very excited about Santa Claus and I am having a hard time telling him Santa does not have any Ghost Buster guns this year. I have bought him a remote control car, which I thought was good value. He also says he wants a game so perhaps we'll make another visit to the toy shop.

I hope you enjoy the festive season.

Love from

Jenny.

Pip appeared to think it was a bad move.

"She said she was interested to know what it was all about and how can she help if she hasn't seen the correspondence?" I argued.

My dear Jenny,

Thank you for your letter sending up the copies of the correspondence during this most unfortunate rumpus in the family, which I may say distresses me very much as I haven't a doubt it would your father and grandfather as well. I cannot say I am any clearer on this matter, which seems to have been blown up from misunderstandings on both sides and I would ask you all to 'wipe the slate clean' and start afresh. Your mother is most distressed - she is as fond of you as any of your brothers or sisters and misses seeing you very much indeed. There is nothing she would like more than for you all to be friends again.

On April 2nd she is going to a lunch party at the Jones's in Oxford. Oxford is not very far from you is it? Could you ask her to come and see you then? I know it is what she would like. Think about it Jenny.

As you have had no contact for so long you probably don't know that early in May your mother is going off to Australia and New Zealand and will be away for a month at least. She is visiting cousins, and also Brian Douglas and his wife, who have had a son in the last few weeks.

I do hope you will be able to bury the hatchet and patch up the differences with the family.

With love to you all.

Ba.

"She's not a stupid woman, how can she say she isn't any clearer on this matter?" I moaned to Pip.

"What good would it do if she did say she understood? Would it improve the situation between you and your mother?"

"I would like a bit of support from someone in my family, especially as I've done nothing wrong."

"As you see it."

"What do you mean?"

"You walked out on her at St Andrews."

"We said goodbye as pleasantly as we could under the circumstances. I don't see how we could have stayed."

"You should have talked to her regarding her intentions over your inheritance."

"I know she wouldn't have discussed it with me."

"How do you know if you didn't try?"

Birthdays have never been a big event in my life. Five of my mother's six children had been born between the 8th December and 27th January, and what with Christmas and New Year thrown in as well, any enthusiasm or money to celebrate my birthday had run out by the end of January. With the current 'unfortunate rumpus' I hardly expected a present, but I should have guessed.

Dear Mummy,

Thank you very much for the lovely sheets that arrived for my birthday. They are always very useful, especially as we never seem to have enough.

I understand you will be in Oxford on 2/4 and I would be very happy to meet you at 1p.m. at the Pizza Parlour at South View Road.

Love Jenny.

Dear Jenny,

I was so pleased to get your letter and hear that the sheets had arrived safely.

Ann Jones's 60th birthday party is a lunch, scheduled 12-2p.m. So could we meet afterwards at 2.30p.m. in the Pizza Parlour for a coffee? If I don't hear from you I'll take it that's OK.

Looking forward to seeing you and hearing all your news.

Much love from

Mummy.

Pip was satisfied. The resolution of the problem was in sight. I must remember to be strong and not let Mum upset me. She was seeing me on my terms. She would be anxious that the meeting pass off amicably, if for no other reason than I was the mother of her grandson and in less than two months of another grandchild. She was an old lady and had no hold over me. How could she upset me? I wasn't to give her power over me.

Wouldn't most people feel nervous given the circumstances?

No, I was to be more adult. I would be surprised at the difference it would make to our relationship if I held my ground politely, but firmly. Psyched up, I left Pip. Going over and over in my head, like a mantra, I repeated her words of wisdom. In a few days I'd meet my mother again.

The evening before the reunion, in a state of high agitation at the prospect of putting the social experiment to the test, I heard the phone ring downstairs and by the time I'd reached it there was a message on the ansaphone.

"Jenny, it's Fay here. You are a complete and utter selfish bitch. There is no other word for it. If you do not contact Mummy after Tuesday when she is back in Scotland and make up to her (and don't mention this message to her), I will teach you what being a bitch is about. I will make your life and Greg's life a misery. How dare you behave like this? I don't care what sort of state you are in. You've no sense for anyone's feelings except your own. You're just a selfish, selfish cow and your husband is no better. Oh God, I'm embarrassed and disgraced that you are even related to me. You're just sick, you're just f....... sick."

The words were bad enough but the venom and naked animosity in her voice were what sent a shiver down my spine.

"Greg come and listen to this," I called, winding the tape back to the beginning and wondering if my ears were deceiving me.

"What is your stupid sister playing at? She must know you are meeting your mother tomorrow? Is she trying to jeopardise the meeting for some reason? I always told you Fay was fruity, if this doesn't prove it, what does?"

"What can she do to make our lives a misery? We never see her from one month to the next; she plays no part in our lives. What does she think she can do?"

"She could do something to Alex, and judging by the tone of her voice I wouldn't put anything past her; she's in a real fury. We have to phone the police and ask them to tell her she can't leave threatening messages like that."

"She can't do anything tonight; let's see how we feel in the morning."

"You just don't phone people up and leave messages of that nature on their ansaphone."

By the morning I felt the same way, and although I dreaded doing it I phoned the police and asked for their help. A constable arrived soon. He agreed that she couldn't leave messages of that nature, but wouldn't it create less acrimony if I spoke to her myself, or persuaded some other member of my family to talk to her? No I didn't think so, my relations with my whole family were pretty acrimonious. I didn't think they would take kindly to a phone call from me complaining about Fay; indeed they would probably condone her remarks. It would have more effect coming from him. I didn't know her address or her workplace, but if he contacted my brother I was sure he would have her number. I was off to Oxford to meet my mother.

We were a one-car family and Greg needed the car that day. I deposited Alex with a friend and caught the bus on its slow journey through the villages to Oxford, arriving in plenty of time.

I had written down the message from Fay and, although the last thing I wanted to do was talk about the bombshell from last night, it must be the first thing we discussed. Was my mother aware of this malicious phone call and did she or did she not agree with it? Were these the sentiments of all my family or just Fay? What was she prepared to do about it? I assumed she would try and shrug it off, change the subject, plead she was still upset by my father's death. I must be strong and firm, thrash it out with her.

I didn't have the appetite for a pizza so I ordered a coffee and concentrated on staying calm while I waited for my mother, going over and over in my mind the carefully planned conversation. For the first half hour I thought my mother might just be late; she was probably as nervous as I was. I ordered a second and third coffee and as the time passed I began to feel very uneasy. Perhaps she had gone to the wrong pizza restaurant. I took all my change and, looking through the yellow pages, I rang round every pizza restaurant in Oxford, but not one restaurant had a customer answering my mother's description. I tried phoning the D. Jones's in the telephone directory, but there were so many of them I gave up and decided to phone Ba in Edinburgh.

"Hello Ba, it's Jenny here."

"Hello dear, how are you?" Her voice was shrill with prudent surprise. To make a long-distance call midday during the week was quite an extravagance and one that would need a good explanation.

"Ba, I'm in Oxford, I've been waiting for Mummy for over an hour now."

"Oh my dear how awful, there's been a mistake. It was yesterday you were supposed to meet your mother."

"No it wasn't, it was today. I sent her a letter and the date was definitely for today. I've got a copy of the letter at home."

"She is staying with Susanna and Dennis for a few days. Did she not phone you when you were not there yesterday?"

"No, but Fay phoned me and left the most foul message you can imagine on the ansaphone. Ba we had to tell the police, we didn't know what else to do."

"Oh no, surely you didn't have to do that?"

"I'll play it to you when I get home, it's still on the tape and it's horrible."

"Oh my dear," she said in dismay. "Listen: I'll phone your mother at Susanna's house after six o'clock and then I'll phone you. It sounds as though it's all been some ghastly misunderstanding. I know your mother was so looking forward to seeing you again and patching everything up. This whole business has been terrible. Did you really have to tell the police?"

"I'll play it to you, we didn't know what it was about, but if Mummy and Fay were waiting here yesterday that explains something. I don't know why Mummy didn't phone me herself and ask me why I wasn't there."

"I'm sure we can sort it all out. I'll phone you tonight, don't waste any more money," she said as the pips went.

At a minute after six Ba phoned, full of remorse. What could possibly have gone wrong? Did I have to phone the police? I played her the message from Fay. How ghastly, what was your sister thinking of?

"Listen Jenny dear, I'm going to phone your mother later on tonight at Susanna's and ask her to contact you."

I must have been bathing Alex, for I didn't hear the phone ring, but I heard the message from my mother on the ansaphone.

"Jenny, I hope your ansaphone is working. I'm so upset that we got our lines crossed and angry with Fay for leaving an unpleasant message. I'll try you again later on."

She did want to see me after all. I'd phone my mother back, suggest she comes to stay on her way back from Susanna's, ask her what she thought of Fay's message. I must stand up to her and not be frightened to discuss things, Pip had been adamant about this. Greg was, if not happy, resigned to her staying for a night, if the situation could be improved.

A few deep breaths and I dialled Susanna's number.

My mother answered. "Jenny I'm so glad you phoned back, what an absolutely stupid mistake I made."

"Mummy I want you to listen to the message Fay sent me." *Strike while the iron is hot,* I thought, as I played it down the phone.

"What is Fay thinking of leaving such a message?" she said in an angry tone.

"I think she is just voicing what everyone else is thinking about me at home."

"Oh no, no. That's not true, it's just Fay being Fay; you know what she is like. She was in a very bad mood. She had driven all the way up to Oxford in her rickety old car, looking forward to seeing you, and then discovered you weren't there."

"I didn't know I was meeting Fay as well. Why was she there, I thought I was only meeting you?"

"She very kindly offered to drive me to Petersfield; it isn't easy to get to from Oxford by public transport, you know."

"Why didn't you phone me. Did you think I stood you up on purpose?"

"No of course I didn't, I thought you had probably had an asthma attack."

"You could still have phoned me even if I'd had asthma," I continued.

"Well I just didn't think about it. Fay had a long drive ahead of her and we just wanted to get going."

"Would you like to come and stay here tomorrow night?"

"I promised Susanna and Dennis I would stay with them until Thursday, I'm babysitting for them tomorrow evening."

"Well come on Thursday then, it won't make any difference to us."

"It's very kind of you Jenny, but I have to get back to feed the dogs."

"Can't Rory or Henry or Phillipa do that?"

"I don't like to ask them, it's coming up to the busy time on the farm. You know how it is with the lambing, but I would like to stay with you before I go to New Zealand and perhaps you could all drive me to Heathrow and wave me off; that would make me very happy."

"All of us wave you off?" I repeated.

"Yes, Greg, Alex and you, drive me to the airport and wave me off."

"I can't answer for Greg, but I suppose Alex and I could."

"I would like that very much, and Greg as well. I must go; Dennis has just made supper for us. I'll phone you again next week when I've got all the details in front of me. I don't want to make any more mistakes over times or dates." And she rang off.

"When is she coming?" Greg enquired ill-humouredly.

"Not for two weeks. She says she has to get back to feed the dogs, but she'll stay here before she flies out to New Zealand and can we drive her out to the airport and all wave her off."

"She can come and stay here if she wants, but I'm blowed if I'm going to wave her off at the airport."

"I thought you would say that," and before the discussion got any further the phone rang again. I lifted the receiver to hear Rory's voice.

"Hello Jenny." I remember thinking how wonderful, he's phoning to apologise. And I was curious to know whether my mother or Ba had told him about the mix-up over the dates.

"Hello Rory, How are you?"

"I'm livid; I can't believe I have such a stupid bitch for a sister. What the hell do you think you were playing at phoning the police and reporting Fay to them? What the Hell do you think that is going to achieve?"

"Rory, I don't have to listen to this. Goodbye." And the phone went down with a bang, before I picked it up and pressed the redial button. Susanna answered.

"Can I speak to Mummy?" I asked in a crisp voice. She wasn't in a hurry to answer the phone this time.

"Mummy, I've just had Rory on the phone swearing at me. I thought you said Fay was only voicing her own opinion and no one else felt the way she did."

"I can't answer for what Rory says. He's an adult and I have no control over what he says to you." Gone was all the bonhomie of five minutes ago.

"I know that, but you can't tell me it is only Fay feeling the way she does when Rory is shouting abuse down the phone at me as well."

"Jenny, I'm in the middle of my supper, I'm going to talk to you another time, goodbye." And down went the phone.

The next day Greg was back in the office to hear that Fay had phoned the previous day, asking for the fax number of the company. She had introduced herself as Greg's sister-in-law, wanting to send a message. So this was how she was going to 'make our lives a misery'. She would ridicule Greg at his office. At least by involving the police we had unknowingly managed to prevent an embarrassing note circulating the office in his absence. What ignominy was she going to dispatch down those telephone lines we'll never know, but I'm confident this was not to be a message full of remorse and heartfelt apologies, for that evening on our return to the house there was another message waiting for our perusal.

"Hi Jenny, it's Fay here. I'm just phoning to say what charming police you have in Thames Valley. They phoned me yesterday. It was a bit strange that you got upset over the use of the 'f' word, but anyway they were very sweet about the whole thing. Rory apparently told them it was all true; everything I said about you, so it seems I have quite a lot of corroboration. Anyway, I was rather disappointed with you playing it to Ba. I mean that was rather upsetting for her, but I think it says more about you than anything else.

"What I really wanted though is one of those silly letters from Greg saying he is going to put a court order on me, because I think that would be quite a joke. We've all had a laugh with the police phoning me, but I would much prefer to have a court order. I think that would be much more fun, don't you? OK I'll speak to you soon. Bye."

We both stood listening in a stunned silence as she rolled out the last sentence with obvious intent, threatening, sinister, malicious, yet all conveyed in a sort of superior, sugary sweetness that set my teeth on edge.

"What game is she playing? I thought my mother's intention was for some form of reconciliation. Has she not conveyed this idea to Fay? Is Fay's idea to drive me out of the family forever, and if so why?"

"I think she's consulted a lawyer to see how far she can go." Greg sighed as I forced myself to replay the message, hardly believing what I was hearing. "Perhaps it was your Aunt Ursula she asked; she doesn't like either of us very much. I'm sure she would have no qualms about encouraging Fay to leave messages like this."

"I'm going to phone my mother up and see what she has to say about it."

My mother didn't answer the phone at her house so I tried Rory's house. Henry answered and handed the phone over to my mother.

"What is it Jenny?" she inquired in a tone of exhaustion.

"Mummy, I've had another message from Fay. I'd like you to listen to it." It was a polite request; I must be polite, for I wanted her on my side, and I played the message hoping her tone would change by the time it was over. But she was at Rory's house, Rory, who she knew had sworn at me down the phone two nights ago in support of Fay; she was at his house having supper.

The message finished and I put the phone back to my ear. "What is Fay playing at?" I asked curiously.

"I don't know and I really don't care. I've had enough of the whole business. I just want to go to New Zealand and marry a nice farmer." I felt shocked, she was thinking of remarrying already; no one in particular, she was just targeting a farmer in New Zealand. Was she considering a divorcee, a widower or an elderly bachelor? What sort of farm did she have in mind? I suppose a sheep farmer was the obvious choice, given her background and the number of sheep there are in that country, or perhaps she wanted a change. Did they have barley barons in New Zealand, the way they do in Britain, or maybe a dairy farmer? The supermarket shelves are full of butter from New Zealand.

"I hope you have a successful holiday," I said, not knowing what else to say.

"Thank you," she replied, "I'll see you in two weeks' time. I'll phone you next week about it. Now goodbye."

149

"What did she say?" Greg demanded as soon as the phone went down.

"She wants to marry a New Zealand farmer," I told him.

"She wants to marry a New Zealand farmer?" He echoed my words in disbelief.

"She wants to go to New Zealand and marry a farmer." The absurdity of the remark demanded repetition. "So soon after Daddy's died. I feel a bit ill at the thought. Doesn't it smack of indecent haste?"

"I'm not interested in her marital plans. What did she say about Fay?"

"She said she's had enough of the whole business and she really doesn't care."

"She doesn't care," he said in a state of shock. "She doesn't care. She is the one person who can put a stop to this idiocy from your sister and she says she doesn't care." He sat back in the chair for a minute before he spoke again.

"Give me that phone, Jenny. I'm going to talk to her. If it wasn't for that last sentence of Fay's message I'd just leave it and forget the whole thing. However, I'm not prepared to have that sister of yours leaving more messages like the one she has tonight, and there is no mistaking that she clearly intends to. Judging by what your mother says she is not prepared to do anything to stop it, so it's up to us."

He pressed the redial button and a moment later he was asking to speak to Jane, a moment's silence before his voice was raised. "She's had enough! I've had enough too. I would like to speak to her." Another moment as he listened, only to echo the speaker's message. "Rory, I'm very tired as well but I want to talk to her."

"The bastard," he hissed. "He put the phone down on me. How dare he? We've got to put a stop to this and the only way is through your mother and she refuses to talk to me."

"I'll have a go," I said, taking the phone out of his hand, and pressing the redial button. Henry answered. "I want to talk to Mummy, Henry."

"She doesn't want to talk to you or Greg. She is very tired after her long journey and she's had enough."

"Enough what?" I asked.

"Enough trouble from you."

"What trouble have I caused?" I asked incredulously, but I never heard the answer. Greg grabbed the phone from me.

"Henry, I want to talk to your mother and if she doesn't talk to me tonight I'll never talk to her again."

"She doesn't want you shouting at her, she is too tired; she just wants to have her supper and go to bed."

"What I'm going to say won't take long and I won't shout at her," he shouted.

"She doesn't want to talk to you."

He took a deep breath and spoke with a forced mildness, "Henry, please will you tell your mother I want to talk to her. I won't shout at her and if she doesn't talk to me tonight I will never talk to her again. Will you tell her all that?"

Greg looked at me as he waited with the phone against his ear tapping his foot impatiently on the ground. His gaze moved to the ceiling as Henry came back to the phone. "You tell your mother I mean every word I said," he uttered with feeling, only to have Henry put the phone down on him as well.

"Listen Jenny, we have to give your family a hard time; it's the only way we can stop these phone calls from Fay."

"I'll phone Fay, ask her what it is she wants to phone me back about."

"She is the one person I really would like to talk to."

Finally she answered the phone; all the sugary sweetness had left her voice.

"What do you want?" was the defensive reaction when she heard my voice.

"Well you could start by telling me why you are so keen on leaving threatening messages on my answer phone?"

"You're a greedy, selfish bitch and you've made yourself ill because you're not getting enough money."

"I don't see why I shouldn't get what I am entitled to."

"You aren't entitled to anything. The money is legally Mummy's and I don't see why you should get anything. Not after the way you both walked out on Mummy at St Andrews because you weren't getting as much money as you wanted."

"Is that what she told you? Well my version of the events is slightly different to that, I can assure you. I only wanted what my father wanted me to have, which was the same as you and the others."

"Why should you? You and Greg are a lot better off than some members of the family."

"Perhaps that is because we are eleven years older than you, and we don't blow our money on expensive parties and holidays."

"Let me have the phone, you're being too reasonable," Greg said as he took the phone off me.

"What the hell are you playing at, leaving these messages on our ansaphone?" he barked down the phone.

"I'm just letting you know what I think."

"I think I'll tell you what I'm going to do, you fax one message through to my office from your company fax machine and I will get lawyers to sue the company you work for, for allowing you to send such material from their fax machine."

"You wouldn't be so stupid!"

"You try me dear, you just try me. If you leave one more message on our ansaphone I will phone you, your mother, your grandmother, and scream as much verbal abuse as I can down the phone at all of you."

"My father would hate you if he knew what you were like now."

"It's difficult to get the opinion of the dead, but I think he might sympathise with me."

"He would consider you just like your wife, sick, greedy and selfish, and livid because you aren't getting as much money as you wanted. He would hate you if he was alive now. You aren't part of our family anyway."

"I couldn't care less. You phone your mother and tell her if she doesn't talk to me tonight I will never talk to her again in my life and she will never see my children."

"We'll see about that," she sneered.

"Yes we will," he screamed, by now he was in a full blown fury.

"I don't want to talk to you anyway."

"Well why do you keep phoning us?"

At that point she put the phone down. Throughout this exchange Greg had paced the room, up and down, like an untamed animal confined to a pen, fierce with a desperate determination to escape, his head pushed down and forward, his shoulders hunched. Up and down, up and down he stalked.

He phoned Rory's number again. Could he speak to Jane? No he could not; she wanted nothing to do with him. That was fine, he wanted nothing to do with her, but if she wanted to see her grandchildren again, she had better talk to him. If he had anything to say he could say it to Rory.

"I want to speak to Jane," he yelled. "I won't shout at her, but if she doesn't talk to me tonight I will never talk to her again. Pass that message on."

The pacing continued, "What is it you want to tell my mother?" I ventured, my eyes following him aghast, for I had never seen this anger before. The answer leapt out violently.

"I want to tell her I am not greedy and selfish, and she had better put a stop to Fay's phone calls, for it is certainly not endearing her to me in any way," he said.

"You bastard," were the next two words to emanate from his mouth. "Listen to what your brother has done." Directing the phone towards my ear. The sound of Beethoven drifted down the line. "He's put the telephone next to the record player."

"Great, we'll just phone Fay again, give her a really hard time and make sure she doesn't ever phone us again."

The phone calls continued. I thought the shouting and screaming would never stop. Messages left on ansaphones, phones slammed down on him and Rory repeatedly leaving the phone next to the record player, always with an introduction by him, "Brahms' 4th, a Strauss' Waltz, Elgar's Pomp and Circumstance." I felt I was suffering a form of shell-shock by the end of the evening. Drained and exhausted as I was, I couldn't sleep.

Emotional paralysis set in. Apathetic and detached, I longed to speak to Pip Barker. I had given her permission to advise me, listened to her rationale, felt enlightened by her judgement of my ordeal, then made the decision to act on her advice. Now it had all gone pear-shaped and I didn't know what to do.

She'd said I could continue with the counselling as long as I needed it and, goodness knows, I needed it now more than ever. I had to snap out of this state.

I phoned the clinic to make an emergency appointment. She could only see me for ten minutes, I was informed. It was better than nothing, I suppose.

I'd never seen her look irritated before. I gave her a brief resume of what had occurred, and then played her the tapes on the cassette player I had brought with me. The effect was electrifying. Her whole body jerked back in the chair with shock, every muscle tensing. Even the wide expanse of dormant bosoms inhabiting the desk quivered as they were wrenched back from their resting place in the only spontaneous movement I had seen Pip make in all the weeks I'd been visiting. The carefully controlled smile lurched for an astonished moment into shocked amazement as a surge of high emotional voltage passed over her face. The textbooks had got it wrong.

She'd taken the model to bits, scrutinised and cleaned all the components according to the manual, pieced it together again, not realising it was connected to the wrong battery, steadfastly refusing to listen to me when I told her the current would be too strong. There was no trip wire; the circuit had burnt out the moment it was switched on. Circuit overload was a matter outside her control. The whole exercise had backfired and she was about to follow suit.

"Have nothing to do with any of them," she snapped at me angrily, "get shot of the lot of them."

"Even my grandmother?"

"Yes, your grandmother as well."

"You don't think she likes me either?"

"I don't think she is particularly concerned about you."

"I'd thought she liked me?" I said, watching her as emotionless and speechless, she shook her head at me in another cruel delivery of another brutal truth; then sitting back in her chair and uncrossing her arms, she looked at me the way she always did at the end of a session.

I understood; there wasn't time for a discussion today.

"When can I see you again?" I asked, feeling panicky. Why wasn't she talking to me? I'd taken a hammering; I needed to talk to her more than ever.

"I'm discharging you. I won't be seeing you again. You're one of my successes," she announced, licking her index finger and drawing an imaginary mark on a board. From where I was sitting I felt like an unmitigated failure and that I was being fired. She had schooled me into believing that for my emotional well-being I should see my family, and convinced me I wasn't the type who could cope without seeing them. I'd taken it all on board and believed her; she was the expert offering me assistance. She'd forced me to face my shortcomings, pulled me apart, with the sole intention of persuading me to stand up to my mother, assuring me it was for the best; and what a horrendous ordeal that had been. Now she was leaving me in smaller pieces than before. She had got it wrong and after all the months of counselling I'd been right. I couldn't see my mother, and this being right gave me no satisfaction. I'd wanted to stand up to her and reap the rewards that Pip, the expert, promised would be mine if I followed her guidelines. I had been closer to the mark than she had, but she wasn't going to chat about it. What was happening to me now seemed infinitely worse than before and now she was abandoning me, not having the courage to discuss her failure.

I went home to lick my wounds. I'd have to move forward on my own.

Greg, who from the start had been ambivalent about counselling, was amazed at her method.

"I thought counsellors listened while the patient arrives at the conclusion on their own."

"She did emphasise it was crisis counselling. Maybe that's different."

"Does that mean creating a crisis?"

"Perhaps Pip decided she didn't have time for me to work it out for myself. After all, it was on the NHS and there is probably a huge backlog of patients waiting for her attention."

Chapter 14

My mother phoned a week later, all giggles and friendliness, to finalise the details of her stay with us before her spouse-hunting tour of New Zealand. The audacity of the woman. After all that had been said last week.

"No," I barked aggressively. I'd given up with polite but firm, it didn't work.

"Oh don't be silly, why not?"

"I'll put it in writing. Then there will be no misunderstanding. Goodbye."

I didn't trust myself to say any more; writing seemed a safer option.

Dear Mummy,

Despite what Rory and Fay seem to think, receiving counselling does not mean you are mentally sick. It is a service to help one realise and accept things. What it has made me realise is that you bully me, put me down and think you can manipulate me by threats and trying to make me feel guilty.

You, Rory or Fay will not bully me, and if Fay thinks she can threaten Greg and me into allowing you to stay she is very much mistaken.

I will not even consider seeing any of you until I have an explanation as to why Rory and Fay think we are greedy, selfish and sick. Why is it acceptable for Fay to try and drive me into a nervous breakdown - as she thought she could do - and to embarrass Greg at work?

Fay made it clear to us you intended to deceive me over my inheritance all along. What she told me on the phone two weeks ago was that I was making myself ill because I was not getting my share of the estate (it was your deception which upset me.) That Greg was not part of the family and she did not like him. Also she considered Greg very selfish and said if Daddy was alive now he would hate Greg. These remarks are unforgivable and the fact

156

that you won't condemn them makes me think you agree with her. Her own hatred and greed motivated these remarks.

We are both very sad about the situation.

Your treatment of Greg has been absolutely foul and until things change I do not want to see you in Henley.

Jenny.

The exhaustion of late pregnancy, when I lay awake at night feeling like a beached whale, left me unable to lie comfortably in any position, in fact, unable to lie at all in certain positions. In the daytime the lack of a downstairs lavatory forced me to make the Herculean task of hauling the immense bulk of my distorted body up to the first floor, twice as regularly as in normal circumstances. I really needed a hoist installed to drag me up the stairs. Had I read a book in some previous incarnation on the joys of pregnancy? It could only have been written by a man. No right-thinking woman could be so thoughtless. And pregnancy second time around wasn't any easier, owing to the first child, the one under your feet, threatening to break your ankle, possibly your leg in two places, if you didn't take proper care of it. This time round I couldn't recline on the sofa at two o'clock in the afternoon with a magazine to read, only to be woken up by Greg four hours later, wondering good-naturedly if I'd made his supper. Fat chance of that now. Alex wanted to go down to the playground, with his bike as well. No I couldn't face carrying the bike all the way home and the thought of pushing it along the road was dire. One false move and I'd land flat on my face with little chance of righting myself unaided. What was a girl to do? Stick to her guns and hack it out while he had a marathon tantrum. There was bribery; I'll buy you an ice cream if you leave your bike at home. No he wanted an ice cream and to take his bike down to the playground. This was not a subject for negotiation, one or the other; he had to make up his mind. Oh no, he'd opted for the bike. Now I couldn't have an ice cream either and it was a sweltering hot day. I'd die if I couldn't have an ice cream. I'd try again. Are you sure you wouldn't rather have an ice cream? I'll buy you an extra large '99', I promise. No he wanted to take his bike and that was that. Perhaps I'd buy him an ice cream anyway. I'll sort out all these behavioural problems after the baby is born; it'll be easier then.

It was at this time, this ghastly time, that I needed guy ropes to hold me in place. I felt that at any moment now every joint below my waist was about to become unhinged with the pressure. I wondered if I would spend the rest of my life walking at a definite backward slant, defying gravity. By necessity I'd developed this stance to counterbalance the enormous mass that pulled me forward. Like a badly stacked hay cart, I felt I could topple at any moment. It was at this time, two weeks before D-day, that Ba phoned.

"Hello Jenny, how are you?"

"Not too bad," I answered lying through my teeth. She had never had children, how could I explain. I'd give anything for a quick release from this discomfort.

"Jenny, I've just had a phone call from Rory." So this wasn't a call of genuine concern, enquiring after my wellbeing, just the polite preamble one makes before launching into the serious business of a telephone conversation.

"Oh!" Every nerve in my body tensed. I should have given her a graphic description of how the baby's head had engaged causing constant pressure on my bladder, the heartburn every time I lay down as the great bulk pushed against my tummy, the stretch marks appearing on my abdomen. Too late now. It was her turn to talk.

"Yes, he was wondering if you had phoned his father-in-law."

"What?" I snapped in disbelief.

"Well, it's awkward dear," she said in a tone of extraordinary concern, full of kindness that implied I could trust her with my confidences. Her only interest, as I knew, was to pour oil on troubled water. "He's had a funny phone call and Rory thought it might have come from you."

"How dare you accuse me of such a thing?" I expostulated in anger.

"I'm not accusing you; I'm just asking you the question." She responded in a clipped tone with all the prim authority of an Edinburgh schoolmistress, checking a cheeky pupil before the entire class got out of hand.

"Well I'm telling you I didn't," I replied emphatically. "I'll have to go. Alex needs me," I told her, putting the phone down quickly.

"Didn't you ask her what this funny message was about?" Greg asked incredulously.

"No I didn't, I was just so cross."

"It must have been pretty bad for Ba to ask you such a question."

"They obviously think it is me who made this call."

"Of course they do, and they'll have told Ba all about the screaming match we had a few weeks ago. You can't let them off with this; they are accusing you of a criminal act."

"What makes it a criminal act?"

"You can't phone people up and make 'funny' phone calls just like that. The police were prepared to intervene to stop Fay leaving us any further messages. The trouble is we don't know what was said to Mr MacDonald. You should have asked Ba what she meant by a 'funny phone call'."

"I thought Ba liked me enough not to ask me such an offensive question, especially as I'm sure she is well aware of how strained things are. Can you imagine her phoning Elizabeth or Susanna or my mother up to ask them such a question?"

"Pip told you to get shot of the lot of them including your grandmother, didn't she? It looks as though your grandmother wants to get shot of you. Perhaps Pip realised something about her that we haven't."

"Like she doesn't have a great opinion of me either."

"I can't think what possessed her to ask such a question. She must have pretty good grounds for thinking it was you. I can only think it was a member of your family."

"Fay, it must have been Fay! You always said you thought she was fruitiest one in our family and I think you are right."

"I think it must be Fay, I can't think who else it could be. If you want to get shot of your family forever, this is a gift."

"All I've got to do is write a couple of letters, one to Rory and one to Ba, refuting their foul allegations, and telling them I want nothing more to do with any of my family ever again."

"It's really Rory who is behind this; he knew exactly what he was doing asking Ba to phone you. You should write the stinking letter to Rory, not to Ba. She shouldn't have phoned you, but remember, she is in her eighties."

"She might be in her eighties, but she is a tough old bird."

"Save the venom for Rory, send her a copy of the letter if you like."

Dear Rory,

I bitterly resent your poisonous allegation of making a 'funny' phone call to your father-in-law. The last thing I want to do is communicate in any form with you or any member of the family ever again. You and the rest of the family have behaved appallingly towards us, you in particular. I believe you were the person who, for your own ends, manipulated Mummy into deceiving me, and you are the root cause of all the problems Mummy and I are suffering.

If you had a shred of decency left in you, you and your father-in-law would withdraw this completely unfounded and unwarranted allegation.

I never want to hear from you again. If you have to contact me do so through my solicitor.

Kevin Riley,
Duke Street,
Henley.

He has been briefed on the situation and is happy to act on my behalf.

Jenny.

And to Ba I sent this note.

Dear Ba,

I enclose my letter to Rory absolutely denying his foul allegation. I have to say I am very disappointed that you saw fit to put this allegation to me. You obviously have a very low opinion of me. Clearly your mind has been poisoned against me.

160

I am eight and a half months pregnant and I do not want any further insults.

I hope you'll respect my wishes.

Jenny.

She did respect my wishes. I never heard from her again.

A few days later, however, a parcel arrived from my mother, posted from Glasgow while she was in New Zealand, with no letter or card, only the sender's name on the reverse of the packaging. A hand-knitted shawl, soft and resilient, knitted with the finest wool. When opened up it looked like a fine intricate lace cloth, a beautiful design radiating out from a central motif. I held it to my face and cried. What was she thinking about, knitting this shawl for my baby, while all the time she was putting me through hell? I folded it up, wrapped it in brown paper and sent it back to Burnside. There would be other grandchildren she could give it to. This was her way, didn't I know it. When matters became too vicious or out of hand, give a generous present and brush the matter under the carpet. She must have learnt about Ba's phone call to me, and the subsequent letters. Perhaps she recognised Fay's handiwork.

The baby was born; a beautiful little girl and I dressed her in Alex's baby clothes. I'd inherited my mother's thrift. However I allowed her one indulgence. I bought her an exquisite knitted shawl.

"What do you make of this?" said Greg, handing over a letter he'd received from Peter Wright.

It started by explaining how reasonable and kind my mother had been to all her children over distributing the assets of Gus's estate, treating them all fairly. He then described how there was one outstanding entitlement for the children of Angus Mackenzie, the capital of Dr Mackenzie's estate when 'Ba Mackenzie's life rent interest comes to an end'. They weren't sure which lawyers would be appointed to wind up the estate, but most likely it would be Robert Brechin, and as Greg had been an executor for Gus Mackenzie's estate they would inform him when the time came.

"He's telling us that if we play our cards properly, I'll come into another big inheritance when Ba dies. Golly, I can't wait."

"Yes, that's how I read it, only it's at the trustee's discretion and you know who that is?"

"Of course, it's Rory. That's only a little catch. I'll suck up to my mother and brother and there'll be no problems. It's so exciting, think of all the money we might get!"

"What do you want to do about this letter?" Greg said

"Do you think we should send a copy of the letter to Ba and see what she thinks?"

"Be serious." He wasn't amused.

"Is there anything to think about? Do they honestly believe we're so greedy they just need to hold out this goody for us and we'll come running to heel? Tell them to get lost; I think it is downright insulting. I'm surprised you even ask me what we should do."

"You know this letter is really from your mother and it's her way of trying to patch things up with you."

Of course I knew it was from her. There was that familiar flavour, stamped across Peter Wright's letter, and leaving a recognisable bad taste in my mouth.

"You aren't going to let them off with this are you?"

"I agree with you. She has dug herself into a hole and now she can't get out. She has been going around telling everyone how greedy and selfish we are, and now she can't bring herself to say we aren't. It would be such a loss of face on her part."

"I know I'm upset about what has happened, but this letter is an example of what they think of us, and I don't like it. If my mother wants to patch things up she could try writing to me herself. Instead she instructs Peter Wright to write to you about something you no longer have any involvement in."

"This letter is misleading and I certainly am not going to let them off with this misrepresentation. I'll write to Peter Wright today and point out the facts as I see them, making it clear that the Deed of Arrangement was not particularly advantageous to you but that the will could not be left as it was since this could have led to arguments! I'll also make it clear I don't want to have anything more to do with your father's estate."

We received a note back from Peter telling him there would be no need for any further correspondence. My mother was having the last word, as usual.

Chapter 15

I also learnt to cope with the juggernaut of motherhood, discovering the slow, awkward, repetitive vehicle and laboriously holding together the precarious joys of child-rearing, interspersed with days which stalled the progress, days full of total frustration and feelings of utter failure, as at every fresh turn of the engine it would cough and splutter more poison into the already polluted atmosphere. Until almost paralysed by fear and anxiety, some strange, unpredictable quirk would unexpectedly jump-start the motor, allowing me the illusion I was at the steering wheel and in control, transporting the business of child-rearing across the years.

There were days when the poignancy of the situation with my family tormented me. What I would have done to rearrange the past. I could not take my children down memory lane to show them where I grew up. They'd never play with their maternal cousins or be spoilt by their maternal grandmother. They would never enjoy the excitement of the farm; the fun of finding new laid eggs, still warm as you picked them up. The lambs, newly born, wobbling awkwardly on their spindly, uncoordinated legs, stumbling instinctively towards their mother, their heads thrown back as they pushed hungrily against the milk laden teats, the low bleating of the ewe as she nuzzled and encouraged her offspring. The magic of the sheepdogs, responsive to unheard commands, accomplished in performing the farmer's bidding, the wonder at seeing a whole flock of sheep floating across the fields like a sunken cloud, wafting this way and that as though caught in a breeze, controlled by the dogs. These dogs with odd black patches splashed over their faces and the irrepressible bounce reminiscent of a circus clown, yet indisputably the cleverest of creatures. Banned from the farmhouse for fear of spoiling them, they kept a silent vigil outside until the farmer emerged to be welcomed with the exuberance of a long lost friend. They jumped up in delight at his reappearance, pushing and rubbing their damp noses into his hands, licking his fingers, asking only for a pat of acknowledgement before dancing round him in a show of gladness.

I remembered the strange and wonderful sight in the late autumn when the heather is burnt in the hills, the unusual light of flames, flickering like a cluster of fairy lights creeping slowly across the undulating hillside as though illuminated from below by some supernatural force, and in the aftermath the puffs of smoke that hung suspended over the blackened ground. Then the start of the long winter with the cold, the drizzle and fog that hung like a grey sheet in front of the landscape and every year the old joke would be repeated 'If you can't see the hills it's raining, if you can see them it's about to rain'. However, these days of melancholy were not so common and I comforted myself in the knowledge of Rory's frustration, dying to develop properties on the farm, but unable to do a thing because I owned 8%.

I had plenty to occupy me. Appearing at customers' doors with my bag of pins, scissors and inch tape, I'd cut loose covers, measure up for blinds or curtains or advise on the pros and cons of different types of bed valances in every conceivable type of house. Occasionally, a smart housekeeper greeted me, at times even a butler would show me in. Some customers would treat my visit as a social occasion and I would be invited to lunch with the whole family, while others would grandly tell me of a corner shop a couple of roads away where I was told ... 'you can buy very nice sandwiches and a cup of tea, so the plumber told me last week'. So I wasn't the only tradesperson packed off down the road!

One charming American husband insisted on introducing me to his children and tried to usher me into the nursery, while I suggested I should perhaps go into the bedroom.

"No, I'll show you the rest of the house in a minute, but come and meet my other daughter first," he insisted. It was difficult to tell him I really didn't want to meet his other daughter, I had children of my own and I was sure his weren't such fine specimens as mine.

"Listen to her on the cello, she plays beautifully," he urged.

Fortunately, I was saved by his wife and wasn't obliged to listen to much of the painful rendition.

"Noel, this isn't the new nanny. Mrs Lorimer, has come to measure up for a new chair cover in the bedroom."

Some kept my number for umpteen years, contacting me when the loose cover finally disintegrated.

"I don't know if you're still making loose covers, you made one for my sofa thirteen years ago. I used to live in St. John's Street; you won't remember me." They were right, I didn't.

"Oh yes, St. John's Street," I say airily, implying that I did.

There is one designer clothes shop in Bond Street that calls me in several times a year to help with the change in their display, and I always leave with the satisfaction of knowing the success of the store is completely dependent on my loose covers, or so the manager would have me believe.

"It's incredible the way you've got all the stripes to match perfectly. Aren't you clever? It makes the sofa look like new."

"Thank you," I would say, smiling graciously, wondering what he would have said if the stripes hadn't matched.

I met people I would never have met in the normal course of life; a boxing promoter who gave me two tickets to watch a boxing match in Hackney; a museum curator from the National Gallery, who, when I enquired about the Titian exhibition, promptly gave me two complimentary tickets; a casting director (as Greg pointed out, sofas were vital in that line of business); property developers who needed work finished on a precise date, to coincide with the decorators completing their work and the property going on the market.

In the early days I made large patchwork beanbags. Cutting out and sewing them up was simple and they sold well in shops. It was the process in between that I found such a palaver, filling the bags up with polystyrene granules and distributing these oversized unwieldy cushions to the shops in my van.

First, I had to phone the wholesaler in Glasgow to check he had the polystyrene granules in stock. After asking the manager on one occasion if he had 'polystyrene balls' I never really felt comfortable again entering the shop. A man of greater sensitivity would not have spluttered and laughed the way he did at my unintentional faux pas. Mortified, I corrected myself.

"I mean do you sell polystyrene granules?"

I was relieved when the bottom dropped out of the beanbag market and I no longer had to face a sneering Mr Lascelles.

Once I was established and experienced as a soft furnisher I had plenty of work, and on the whole I enjoyed it. There were the more tight-fisted ladies who would examine my work with a fine-tooth comb, trying to pick holes in it (metaphorically) and hoping to pay less than the agreed bill. However they were the exception. More often the customer would treat me as though I was doing them the greatest favour.

"We've wanted loose covers for months. It's so difficult to find anyone these days, then I saw Joyce's new covers that you made last month and she gave me your name and number. I'm so delighted to have got hold of you."

I commandeered a large back bedroom, installing a work table in the centre of the room, which in fact took up most of the space, and the cumbersome industrial sewing machine parked in front of the window looked out over the garden; a large fitted cupboard stored the tools and essentials of my trade. Underneath the work table was now Millie's house, where she and her dolls spent hours in a happy contented world of their own playing with requisitioned bits of piping cord and snatched remnants of fabric. Meanwhile I, from the nerve centre of 'Jenny Lorimer Enterprises', machined away, watching the quietly changing kaleidoscope of colours as the seasons gently turned the garden. Even in the depths of winter the holly berries burst on to the scene with a warmth and vibrancy to attract the dullest eye, the winter-flowering jasmine speckled yellow against the dappled green of the hedgerow and the viburnum stood strong and powerful against the sombre green of its leaves. These unseasonable flowers in the drizzle and gloom of winter cheered me as much as the abundance of summer. Here I listened to the radio for hours.

There was a continuity and satisfaction of working with customers to whom I had been recommended by previous customers, and like a genealogist I could trace a line of customers back for years. I enjoyed my work, even though my plan had not been to marry a man with feminist sympathies, who didn't see why I should be deprived of the pleasure of pursuing my own career. I was on a treadmill, not an unenjoyable treadmill, but a

167

treadmill all the same and, sometimes, I felt it was undignified to make loose covers at my age. What else could I do? I would turn my hand to satirical poetry. I'd read A.A. Milne - it seemed quite simple. A little study of the political landscape of our time . . .

This socialist man, could this be he?
A man of Oxford pedigree.
However hard the party tries,
They'll not be able to disguise,
That Tony Blair is rather smug
And ever so sure that he's no mug.
His grace and eloquence and charm,
So far haven't done us any harm.
I really don't think it's cricket
To compare his looks to Margaret Beckett.

This would-be leader of our country,
Will reduce us all to penury.
He'll tax what money that he can,
By bankrupting the common man,
But generally will seem to lack
The need to keep us in the black.
Now please don't go blaming him,
It's just the party that he's in.

Now if his name was Hestletine
I'd make this such a flattering rhyme.
I know this isn't very kind,
I had to make some lines that rhymed.
I'm just a concerned working wife
Who isn't wanting any strife
But do you think this worries him?
No, he only wants to win.

I thought it was rather good and decided *The Times* was the paper to appreciate my particular genre. I imagined the critics would proclaim it a dazzling success, worthy of comparison with I don't know who. I could envisage my future embroiled in disputes with

rival publishing firms, vying for the publishing rights of my works; while the TLS wrote weighty articles evaluating my particular style. Flocks of scholars would beat a path to my door, eager to delve into my mind and analyse my inner thoughts and I would regale them with my poetry. I started to compose my next poem while waiting for the cheque to arrive. There would probably be a fortnightly slot for my work culminating in an anthology of *'The complete works of Jenny Lorimer'*.

It was a blow when *The Times* returned my poem. Not to worry, I knew the *Weekend Guardian* printed poems. In a week or two those *Guardian*-reading mums would be approaching me in the playground in awe.

"I didn't know you were a poet Jenny."

And I would reply nonchalantly, with all the modesty of a published poetess, "It's what I do in my spare time."

Wouldn't they be impressed?

The Guardian too was unable to give me the break I needed to launch my new career. So it wasn't to be a case of curtains on curtains. Oh well, what would the soft furnishing world be without me? I would have to learn to be undignified. Still it's sad to think of all the poems I might have written - if only!

Chapter 16

Life wasn't so bad. I loved Henley, the architecture, the streets, the houses. We had a local theatre, the cinema, the quaint olde-worlde pubs, the smart dress boutiques and the nonsense shops. Henley has followed the trend of other rural towns in helping the ailing farming community. On the last Thursday of each month the market place is decked out with farmers' stalls, for the locals to purchase agricultural products denied a place on the supermarket shelves; finely sliced fresh trout, a small selection of wines grown and bottled locally, organically grown herbs. From one corner of the square wafts the tantalising aroma of whole pig roasting. Porky rotates round and round, spitting fat in all directions and for only £3 one can enjoy a fresh roast pork bap.

For the more energetic there are the tennis courts and sports fields and, of course, what puts Henley on the map, the rowing clubs and 'The Henley Royal Regatta'. This is when Henley comes alive.

In early May, large blue and white striped tents appear, wide, long, low-slung tents parked along the water's edge to house the precious boats. A milestone in the Henley calendar, only eight weeks to the Regatta. Several weeks later, booms emerge on the river, a barrier dividing the river into two tracks, stretching the full length of the reach. Next comes the bunting, zigzagging precariously across the narrow streets, closely followed by the removal of the swans. These haughty, bad-tempered beauties are rounded up and sent packing for the duration. The oarsmen will be arriving any day now, lanky giants with shoulders like cart horses' withers, unable to walk side by side down the narrow pavements for fear that their unsynchronised steps may end in a mid-air collision of those overdeveloped scapula muscles. These sportsmen, who move in splendid harmony, effortlessly surfing the water when half submerged in unstable skiffs, cruise the streets awaiting their allotted time to plough up and down the river with their coach cycling alongside on the tow path with a loud speaker strapped horizontally across his shoulders like a school satchel, barking instructions across the water to the crew.

He ignores intrepid pedestrians strolling along with their dogs for their daily constitutional; the dogs disappearing sporadically to nearby trees and posts, justifying the compulsory nature of their owner's regular exercise.

In the two weeks leading up to the event, when the town would swell and vibrate with the influx of virile bodies clothed in skimpy T-shirts and even skimpier shorts, revealing muscular, hirsute limbs, pumping testosterone into the atmosphere, Henley seemed at its least regal.

When the children were in bed I'd walk down to the bridge and watch the crews practise, silhouetted against the flickering water in the evening light, skating along the river surface like some strange winged insect. Ripples of water frolicked impishly from each blade as the oarsmen pulled, pulled, pulled, down the long reach towards Marsh Lock, my eye drawn along with the flow of the boat.

Then on the first Wednesday of July the Regatta starts. The traffic is re-routed as thousands of cars descend on the town. The cricket ground, local fields and, at the weekend, even the school playground are transformed into car parks, as countless rowing enthusiasts make their annual pilgrimage to Henley.

On the Saturday, we would hire a boat and join the hordes of day-trippers devoted to the serious business of having fun on the river. Crafts of all sizes jostled on the narrowed waterway, avoiding the flashy gin palaces and the paddle steamer bursting with gay young things jiving precariously to the jazz band on board. Dipping the oars carefully into the water we manoeuvred our way, cautiously trying to avoid a collision, to a space along the boom to moor the boat. From this vantage point we watched the races.

As the afternoon wears on and the alcohol consumption kicks in the decibel level rises, with acquaintances shouting out to each other as they drift past, the hand-eye co-ordination deteriorating and boats bumping into other boats. Horns are blown and a couple of people usually end up in the water. One year we witnessed a youth, full of high jinks, stand up in his boat and expose himself to the corporate entertainees in the smart marquees, a sight they most likely had not expected to see. I suspect the sausage rolls looked a lot less appetising as a consequence.

And where did this influx of mankind stay, you may ask. Mainly the visitors stay in Bed and Breakfast accommodation, as the ladies of Henley officially become 'Regatta landladies'. Exempt from the normal Berkshire and Oxfordshire fire regulations pertaining to guesthouses, we're merely asked to use our common sense, as though sensible ladies wouldn't do that anyway.

I join the serried ranks, packing my children into my workroom for a week. My first time as a Regatta landlady was a terrifying experience. I twittered away nervously explaining I was not a professional Bed and Breakfast lady, anxious to pre-empt any complaints. I needn't have bothered. The guests were just grateful to find a bed within striking distance of the Regatta. Over the years I've played host to every type of visitor. Spectators come to enjoy the ambience, the oarsmen; the oarsman's girlfriend arriving late on Saturday afternoon for the Regatta ball, interested in the oarsman, but not his performance on the river. The veteran dressed up like an ageing Billy Bunter character, cap at a jaunty angle, the stripy blazer he'd worn thirty years ago with his team secured precariously by the centre button, straining under pressure against the corresponding buttonhole. His portly waist confirming that he might have stopped rowing, but hadn't stopped eating. I've had them all.

After their breakfast I'd watch the guests swan off in their finery to the Stewards' enclosure, where a strict dress code applies. Ladies have to wear skirts or dresses with hem lines at or below their knee. No trouser suits or culottes are allowed. Men have to wear blazers or jackets with shirts, ties properly knotted at the neck. Vigilant stewards, transported hotfoot from Royal Ascot, attired in dark grey suits and top hats, stand guard at the entrance to the enclosure, Jeeves-like, enforcing the rules.

"Excuse me Sir, your tie." And mobile phones are a definite no-no.

The rationale when queried is: 'To maintain the atmosphere of an English garden party of Edwardian times'. And so they do, with the flannels and decorative blazers, topped with the panamas and boaters, mingling by the water's edge, enjoying a Pimms with the swirling floral dresses and the magnificent millinery designed to compete with the boats for the limelight. Wondrous three-dimensional sculptures created from the best materials, the result of dedication and skilled workmanship producing fine lines, elegant curves and an exact trim. This is the Henley experience, quaint flamboyance overlaid by tradition. Then, when it's over, we, the exhausted Regatta landladies, after all the preparation, the anticipation, the excitement of the great event, would emerge exhausted in the anti-climax and enquire of each other.

"How was it for you?"

Over the years I've become acquainted with most of my neighbours and they aren't so bad. Michael and his wife run an import/export business, very dollar-sensitive Michael informed us, and their mood swings appear to go up and down with the value of the pound. Sarah, whose husband's business is manufacturing colostomy bags, has the smartest house in the street; obviously there is a lot of money in colostomy bags. Timothy, like several others, looks constantly exhausted, the commute to the City proving more exhausting than he'd reckoned. Jeremy flies long-haul flights from Heathrow. Millie assured me in no uncertain terms that she'd learnt from Kate, his daughter, that he was going to be king next week. She was adamant; he was definitely going to be king next week. On his return from China the misunderstanding became clear; he had been to Peking.

Alice introduced us to the fun of pond dipping. Ponds are a lot more than oversized puddles; they are habitats, rich in vegetation, teeming with wildlife. Investing in one-pound nets, we spent hours leaning over ponds with our children, watching them chase the nimble young frogs through the water, getting the nets embroiled in weeds, forcing them under rocks until finally a raucous squeal of delight forewarned that a squat little amphibian would soon be airborne, hoisted out of its slimy habitat and held high for everyone to admire. Little rivulets of smelly, stagnant water would run out of the net, down the cane, across the little hand clinging tightly to its catch and career onwards to the

173

armpits and down the tummy, giving rise to yet more noisy laughter, before the poor terrified creature was dumped back in its natural abode.

In our back garden we put down compost, turned the soil, planted seed potatoes, watered the ground and waited. The excitement when shoots appeared, the thrill as we watched the stalks grow and thicken, the leaves multiply and the flowers arrive. We dug up the first potato plant. The anticipation was great but the product minuscule, lots of little marbles of potatoes rolled between the prongs of the garden fork. We would have to exercise some patience and wait a few more weeks before we could enjoy the fruits, or in this case the vegetables, of our labours. Fired by this success, we cultivated a notion of self-sufficiency, deciding the next year to plant carrots, and went through the same procedure again, but when harvesting time came we were devastated; all that toil and labour had produced only stunted and deformed carrots. If we had lived near Sellafield I would have believed they had mutated; as it was, I suspected our neighbour's rabbits of damaging them, before Mother Nature had completed her task. We recycled them in the compost and reinforced our fence. Now we grow rhubarb, gooseberries, herbs, and potatoes, plants that are resilient and tenacious, and flourish without too much work.

When the weekends come we take to the roads and explore the countryside, the wooded winding lanes of South Oxfordshire that lead to the Chiltern hills, undulating and serene, long swathes of fertile green slopes falling elegantly to the villages nestling quietly in the folds of her skirts. Villages that rest there tranquil and demure, names whispered down from Saxon times, rich earthy sounds that loiter in the mind, Frieth, Turville, Fingest, a haven from the bane of motorways, high-rise flats and flashing neon lighting. Cradled in a time warp, they doze contentedly, a window on the past and an escape from the present. We traced the foothills, wandered the bridle paths and rights of way, and, like voyeurs, we studied the gardens that back onto the paths, the vegetable patches and the greenhouses, the compost heaps and the cold frames; very middle-aged pursuits.

Middle-age also meant that after a night out on the town I didn't bounce back the way I had once, and my waist had disappeared. So when Greg tactfully advised me to join the health club if I wanted to squeeze into the same dress I'd worn last summer, I put him straight.

"What you're looking at is called middle-aged spread and it takes place in women of my age, and although I'm not oblivious to the advance of time, the quest for youth is not one of my priorities."

Put tartly like that, one would assume he would drop the subject.

"Why don't we go shopping for a new dress next Saturday?" he suggested, trying a different tack.

"If my clothes don't fit me as well as they used to, too bad. It's a minor irritation, not a matter that troubles me! You didn't marry me for my looks did you?" That did the trick.

What I do know is that, when Mother Nature's cruellest trick caught up with me, it shook me to the core. I could no longer thread needles with the ease I once did. The effort of focusing as I cut along the grain of fabric left me with eyestrain. The optician put me through my paces. I needed glasses for close work, reading, that sort of thing. There was nothing wrong, just a normal ageing process.

"Margaret will show you our selection of frames and help you if you have any queries."

I wasted none of Margaret's time. Instinctively I knew the frames for me. I looked in the mirror. My face froze. It must be a trick of the light? It could not be true. I felt my stomach turn. Through the frames I could see the same small dark eyes as hers gazing back at me. I screwed up my eyes, wrinkled my face. The effect was useless; it was her. Ursula Stone was staring back at me. I comforted myself with the knowledge the resemblance was only superficial.

Chapter 17

There was an unusually loud knock at the door. I opened it, irritated at the sight of what I took to be the back of a rep. A tall, well-built man, wearing a suit, and as bald as my father had been, turned round.

"Hello Jenny," he said with a forced lightness, and moved forward as though to cross the threshold.

"Christ," I uttered, slamming the door shut. It was Henry.

I wondered what to do. He knocked again even louder. I hurried through to the kitchen and away from him and the front door, as though the physical distance would somehow protect me, and prayed he would leave. He started shouting through the letterbox.

"Jenny, I want to talk to you, let me in!"

Trying to calm my nerves I shouted back, "Go away. I don't want to talk to you!"

"I want to talk to you. Do you hear me?" he yelled, continuing his assault on the door.

I phoned the police. Five minutes later he unexpectedly stopped knocking. A minute later a police car pulled up. At last I felt safe.

A policeman and a policewoman climbed out of the car and headed towards the house.

"He's only this minute gone; he must have seen you driving down the road and decided to disappear," I told them apologetically.

I invited them into the house and they followed me through to the sitting room. Sitting down, they waited for an explanation. The policeman, fitting comfortably into the armchair, relaxed back on the feather cushions, his elbows resting easily on the arms of the chair as he looked casually around the room. His companion sat opposite him on the sofa, her legs pressed neatly together gazing at me with interest. There was a sort of docile sociability in their postures; this was Neighbourhood Policing in action.

"Can you explain what happened?" the woman asked as her colleague languidly turned his head to look at me.

I delivered a brief history as they sat and listened, with a professional, unresponsive gaze.

"What can I do to stop it happening again?" I asked pathetically.

"I agree, your brother's behaviour constitutes harassment, but as we didn't actually see him we're powerless to do anything."

"Could I take out an injunction to stop him?" I wondered.

"You must have good grounds to be given an injunction. It's expensive, it only lasts six months and, on top of that, it's difficult to enforce, and there is not much we can do if it's broken," the man explained.

"My mother is behind this visit, could you phone her up and talk to her?"

"No, we can't. She would think we were bonkers, and tell us to mind our own business."

"We don't like to get involved in family affairs," the policewoman intervened tactfully. "I think the best thing would be for us to look for your brother between here and the station and warn him not to pester you again, I'm afraid we can't do any more than that."

"I'm sorry to have involved you in this, but I didn't know what else to do."

"That is what we are here for," the man said kindly, as he got up to leave.

The moment Greg walked in the door that evening I told him of Henry's unwelcome visit. He crumpled down in the chair, frozen for a couple of minutes.

"He didn't come all this way just to talk to you. They are after something and it's probably your shares in the farm."

Breakfast was always a noisy time as the children would argue over who was to tell Daddy that breakfast was on the table. As the letters dropped through the letterbox there was a five-minute dogfight as they fought over whose turn it was to bring them into the kitchen. I would sort out the bills, bank statements and junk mail, rarely anything of interest, but today, as I opened a plain white envelope addressed to me and read Rory MacKenzie and Torlochan Farm Ltd., I gathered my wits and read it nervously.

My mother had appointed a new firm of accountants for Torlochan and they thought I should sell my shares in the company to Rory for a reasonable £2,500, as the company only made modest profits

"I've always known that one day Rory would make an approach for my shares, but this offer is absurd. They must know I won't consider such a ludicrous sum."

"They don't expect you to accept that price; they expect you to bargain with them, and then you'll feel pleased when they agree to £10,000."

"Well even that price is ridiculous."

"They've set the offer far too low. There is no point trying to negotiate from that level. If they had made it £15,000 we could have taken it from there, but, as you say, £2,500 is absurd."

"It's immoral to offer me such a low amount. I hope I wouldn't do that to anyone."

"Jenny, it's a business transaction, nothing more than that; you must decide what you want to do."

"Perhaps it is only a business transaction, but I'm not an anonymous number on a share certificate, I'm her daughter that she hasn't seen for years because of a dispute over money, and now it looks as though she is spoiling for another fight. When is it all going to end?"

"Rory wants the farm for himself; then he can make a killing doing up properties and selling them off with a few acres of land. That is what I suspect he has in mind. Why don't you give the shares to the children? That way your mother can't accuse you of being greedy, and they won't be able to pursue the children in the courts as they are minors."

"That's a brilliant idea, I'll do that."

"I don't know how feasible it is, you'll have to phone your accountant and talk to him about it."

"What can I do for you?" Mr Dockerill was not big on small talk.

I briefly told him the story and asked about the possibility of donating my shares to my children.

"I think that is a non-starter, as it would require the agreement of the directors, in this case your mother and brother. If you like I could write to Neeveys on your behalf, asking them to send copies of the accounts for the last six years, and tell them to invite you to the AGM."

"Yes, that's a good idea. Could you do that?"

I sat down and studied the documents in front of me as best as I could, but with a layman's eye it made no sense. It appeared that, every year, the accounts concluded with a sum announcing a total loss. I would have to wait for Greg's return to interpret the figures.

"I don't believe it. Every year they seem to make a loss. Did you notice that they have reduced the rent from £8,400 per annum, when your father ran the farm, to £1,500 per annum? I don't know much about farming, but that rent seems very low."

"Why did their accountant say they were making modest profits when they transparently aren't?"

"He probably just took instructions from Rory."

"How can they keep it running as a company when it makes losses every year?" I asked in amazement.

"There's a deposit account which had over £40,000 in it when your father died. It looks as though they've been eating into it over the last six years."

I phoned Mr Dockerill to see if our understanding of the accounts was correct.

"Yes," he agreed, "the company is running at a loss every year. The rent is unreasonably low. If the tenants can't pay a proper rent you get new tenants. It's as simple as that. The courts will take a very dim view of the way the company is run. There is such a thing as oppression of minorities, which I think is the case here. You really ought to go to the next AGM and insist that the company charges a fair rent."

"I wouldn't have the nerve to attend an AGM."

"I would be happy to attend the AGM on your behalf."

"I don't want to get embroiled in an expensive legal battle," I said.

"Usually just a bit of sabre-rattling does the trick in these cases," he replied.

I drafted a letter and phoned Mr Dockerill to check that it was acceptable.

Dear Mr MacIver,

I have now received the accounts. I note that the accounts show that the company has made losses over the last few years and has not, as you stated in your letter, been making only modest profits. I note that the rent paid to the company has been reduced from £8,400 to £1,500 per annum, representing a rent of less than £4.00 per acre. It is hardly surprising that the company constantly makes losses, when the rent has been so reduced. I believe that the directors, in agreeing to this rent, have not been acting in the best interest of the shareholders. Because the rent has been set so low it is absurd to value the company on the basis of its current profitability.

I would be grateful if you would send me no more unsolicited letters on this matter and would be grateful if you would remind the directors of their legal obligations to send me the accounts on an annual basis, to invite me to the annual general meeting and to run the company for the benefit of the shareholders.

I look forward to receiving the next set of accounts when they are issued.

Yours sincerely,

Jenny Lorimer.

"I'm not a lawyer," Mr Dockerill said, "however I think the letter is fine. You've told them you don't want to sell your shares, you're not happy about the way the company is run and you've sent a strong warning shot across their bows with the last paragraph. You've done the groundwork if you need to take legal proceedings at a later date. Their accountant will warn them that legally they would have trouble defending the way they have managed the farm so far."

Chapter 18

Dear Jenny,

Over the past two to three years I have given the sum of £20,000 to each of the non-farming members of the family and I would have liked you to be included in this arrangement. I had hoped to make you a gift in March but I am now in a position to make it at the end of November.

It is a source of great sadness to me that there is no contact with you and whatever you may feel about me you will always be my daughter and I have a mother's feelings for you.

Yours sincerely,

Jane.

I felt only happiness; we could heal the rift and be friends. I realised how deprived I'd been, how much I missed having any family. I'd been sitting so long on a hard pew, I had become accustomed to life this way; severe, unyielding, until it became the norm.

This letter signalled a great change in my life. Suddenly I was reclining on a top-of-the-range sofa, of richly woven tapestry and goose-down cushions, buoyed up by all this unexpected kindness. All the severity, the hardness of the last six years evaporated in a vapour of euphoria. I allowed myself to fantasise on the reconciliation. I must compose a letter, tell her of my gladness at the thought of seeing her again, and invite her to stay, thank her for the offer of money. There would be the initial awkwardness after such a period but it would pass. I must write soon, let her know my feelings. But my bones were not used to this sumptuousness; the goose down gave me no support as I lounged back in comfort. Luxuriating in this ease was like a feast when enough would suffice. I felt misgivings, rumblings, I didn't trust this opulence. Was it because I'd adapted to the basic and now my body could not respond to such extravagance?

Was it just the imagined pleasure in having a loving mother or was it the offer of £20,000? I felt ashamed that, underlying these feelings, the true motivation might have been money. A more analytical mind than mine could reason logically. If she could only tell me we were not greedy and selfish I could happily accept the money.

A small doubt began to creep in. I'd sit on it firmly and pretend it wasn't there, only I hadn't considered the highly sprung upholstery. The vibrations radiated, sending a shiver up my spine. Try as I might to recapture the ecstasy of only a few days ago I couldn't. There was a tingling in my toes, pins and needles developed. I wriggled my feet but the cramp had got hold, the back of my calf was in spasm. Recumbent on this sofa I needed no muscle tone, I could flop like a rag doll, limbs askew, but my body was rebelling against this unfamiliar comfort.

Like a hallucinogenic drug, the effect had worn off and now I was plunged into deeper despair than before. I must return to the pew; not luxurious, it was honest and upright, giving no false comfort, only the plain facts. I discovered there was more comfort in this stalwart woodwork than in all the luxury of the sofa. There was no pretence here, no fabrication, no concealing the truth, no hidden springs starting a false motion, no decorative façade to cover the coarse framework. From this hard bench there was a harmony, a perfect balance. The muscles maintaining a stillness, not rigid, but upright and comfortable, heightening my stature.

A gift is a gift. If my mother wanted to give me £20,000, why not do so? Why withhold a cheque? She could have included it in the letter. There must be an ulterior motive. I felt it in my bones. The idea came to me in an instant.

I phoned Stirling council.

"Yes, Rory Mackenzie at Torlochan has detailed planning permission for two properties."

"Can you send me copies of the planning permission?"

The plans duly arrived and on the back of a copy I wrote to my mother.

Did you take this into consideration when you offered me two and a half thousand pounds for my shares?

All students of art learn early in their training the importance of negative spaces that trace the curves and cusps, vital for measuring the relationships between the positive shapes, giving a balance to the overall composition. The response from Jane never came, and so the outline became clearer. Her letter confessing motherly feelings and an offer of £20,000 was the negative shape that highlighted the absurdity of my wish for a reunion with my family.

Dear Mother,

I refer to your letter. You make two points, that you have no contact with me and that you have a 'mother's feelings' for me. If you have a 'mother's feelings' this dreadful situation should never have arisen.

a) *You tried to cheat me over my father's will.*

b) *Fay told me in no uncertain terms that I am not part of the family. You are aware of what she said and you have never told me that you disagree with her.*

c) *You gave me absolutely no support when Ba Mackenzie, on Rory's instructions, phoned to ask me if I had been making 'funny' phone calls to his father-in-law.*

d) *When we failed to meet in Oxford did it occur to you that I could have had a car accident? If you had a mother's feelings for me you would have phoned to find out what had happened. This is precisely what I did as soon as you did not appear the following day.*

I now find that, in addition to the above, you are trying to cheat me out of shares. Under the circumstances, I do not want to receive £20,000 from you. I am unable to change this terrible situation, which never would have arisen if you had a mother's feelings for me.

Jenny.

Chapter 19

We were off on holiday in two days time and with hindsight it wasn't the ideal time to send the letter. On our return Greg found an opened letter in his office. It was a pity that Jane did not write 'Private and Strictly Confidential' on the envelope.

Dear Jenny and Greg,

Thank you for your letter. Let me explain about bereavement. No one can guess what the loss of a spouse is like until they have experienced it - the anguish, vulnerability and the need for comfort and affection from friends and family.

After our holiday in St Andrews - my first without your father - you left me alone, weeping, devastated. You never bothered to ring or write to find out if I had got home safely or was feeling better. You made a phone call to Peter Wright's office to say all future communications about your father's estate were to go through the lawyers and then Greg's letter of resignation as an executor came. Imagine my shock and distress to receive a long letter all about the Deed of Arrangement, polite perhaps, but extremely cold and unfriendly.

I have never understood the accusations of cheating and deceit over your father's will, which you instigated. If you were deceived and cheated so were Elizabeth, Susanna, Fay and Henry but I have received no accusations from them. You were given 8% of the Torlochen Farm shares and your father hoped that Rory would be able to buy some of you out. If you wish him to buy your shares you must negotiate a price.

As to our abortive meeting in February - it was a genuine mistake (one I have made on sundry other occasions) and for which I apologised the next night on the phone from Susanna's. I'm afraid at the time I took your non-appearance as yet another of your rejections and I most certainly did not 'incite' Fay to make her abusive phone call. I had told her the affair was between you and me and she was not to interfere, but I cannot control adult children.

As for (c) I haven't the faintest idea what you are on about. It must have been something that happened while I was in New Zealand.

Rory's income as a livestock farmer must be a fraction of Greg's. The others have all received £20,000 from me and I should like you to receive the same. My offer stands till the end of the year but if you still wish to reject it then I shall divide it between the others.

Perhaps the moment has come to try a little Christian forgiveness?

Love from,

Mummy.

Hadn't Pip told me my mother would always blame me, whatever happened? How right she was. I decided to write the definitive letter. If anyone ever tried to persuade me to see her, I'd simply refer to it.

Dear Mother,

It is preposterous for you to announce that you have never understood my allegation that you tried to cheat me over my father's will. We left St Andrews because you had indicated to Greg that you intended not to carry out my father's wishes. Greg resigned as executor because you were not going to carry out my father's wishes and at no time did you or any of the other executors write to him to advise that he was wrong about this.

I then wrote to you to seek your confirmation that you would carry out my father's wishes. My letter was as warm as it could be under the circumstances and I expressed my sorrow that I had to write it.

Rory then replied that you were too upset to respond and that all correspondence henceforth was to be through lawyers. If at that stage you were going to carry out my father's wishes you would certainly have said so, unless you were deliberately trying to create a terrible problem.

The only response was that John Anderson phoned Greg to say that he thought you had changed your mind about implementing my father's wishes and that you were thinking of telling me to 'get lost'. By that stage I had already posted a letter to you saying that I could never see you again because of your deception. Surely my position could not have been clearer or easier to understand and it is obvious that at this stage you were still going to deceive me.

I have never alleged that you tried to deceive the others. I believe that each of them had their own motives for going along with the deception and I know some of them even found it funny. This is what is so terrible about this situation. It was not just you who wanted to deceive me - I believe it was my whole family.

Subsequently, Fay told us that you had intended to deceive us, and that she thought it quite reasonable because we were better off than some of the other members of the family. What possible motive can I have for an allegation of deceit against my own mother unless it were true?

Can you imagine my complete dismay when, on the evening before our meeting in Oxford, I received a torrent of abuse? At the time I had no idea of what lay behind this call, but I was shocked by the depth of animosity which it contained when, all along, it had been our strong desire to carry out my father's will on an amicable basis. When I received a call on the following day with the same animosity, in spite of their knowing why I was not at the meeting, I knew my relationship with my family was almost certainly at an end. I knew very well that Fay's views could not be hers alone but had to be shared to a greater or lesser extent by every member of my family. I asked you to visit me the evening following our abortive meeting, but you said that you had to return home to feed the dogs.

As far as I was concerned the meeting in Oxford was very important. Your letter seems to place the same regret at missing that meeting as missing an appointment with a dentist.

It is untrue that I phoned Peter Wright to advise that henceforth all communications should be through the lawyer. I phoned to say that communications should be in writing to avoid any misunderstandings and I think your misunderstanding on this proves that this was the correct thing to do.

Regarding Ba's phone call, I am astonished that you have no knowledge of it, and disappointed that you are not sufficiently interested in resolving the situation to ask Rory or Ba what had happened.

I cannot comment on Rory's income relative to Greg's as you did not tell me Rory's income. However, if it is of any comfort to you, I have no doubt that the market value of the farm and its properties is well in excess of any money we will ever have. As you should be well aware the value of £36,000 placed on the farm was a fantasy for the purposes of dealing with the Revenue, to reduce any inheritance tax, and would never have been accepted if not for the Deed of Arrangement.

My father's will was much more generous to Rory than any of the others and I have never had a problem with this. At the same time I am sure he did not want me to be cheated out of money.

I do not understand your reference to Christian forgiveness, since, as far as you are concerned, you have not done anything wrong, so how can I forgive your non-existent sin, your deceit and my upset are all a figment of my imagination.

If you want the position between us to improve, as I do, then the appropriate actions must come from you. There is nothing I can do to change the situation and it will persist for as long as you want it to.

Jenny.

Chapter 20

NOTICE IS HEREBY GIVEN . . .

The AGM for Torlochan was to be held at Chisholm and Davis W.S. in Edinburgh, and, thoughtfully, they had even included a proxy form 'in accordance with the articles of association'.

Mr Dockerill would go on my behalf.

"I want the annual accounts sent to me on time, and the rent raised to a market level," I told him.

"Would you happen to know what a reasonable rent would be for the farm?"

"No, but I can find out. I still keep in touch with Rose and she'll have a good idea what it should be."

Mr Dockerill had been Rose's accountant until her marriage to a farmer, and it was at Rose's suggestion that he had become my accountant.

"That would be a great help."

"Farming is going through a difficult time at the moment," Rose told me, "and to be honest we make more money out of the bed and breakfast and letting the cottage than we do out of the farm. I see your brother and sister-in-law are doing farmhouse holidays and bed and breakfast. They'll do well out of it, Torlochan is a much larger farmhouse than ours."

"How do you know what they are up to?" I asked in surprise.

"I see them advertising in the same holiday brochures that I advertise in," she explained.

"I can't imagine Rory doing bed and breakfast; I'd have thought he was far too grand for that."

"I'm not, the money is very good and they are in a fantastic location. They'll be turning people away during the summer."

I phoned Mr Dockerill and gave him the realistic rental value of the farm land of £20 per acre. I told him about the bed and breakfast business, the cottage that could be rented out and detailed planning for two more properties to be built.

The meeting was the next day; he'd phone me as soon as he returned to the office.

"Your mother was there, your brother Rory, your sister Elizabeth and the lawyer. The first thing your mother wanted to know was why we were having the meeting. I told them they had a legal obligation to have an Annual General Meeting every year and invite all the shareholders. I asked to see the minutes of last year's AGM and was told they hadn't had one, in fact they told me they have never have had an AGM. I instructed them that in future they must hold an AGM within ten months of the accounts being issued and that you were to be invited.

"We then went over the accounts. I made it very clear that I considered the rent was far too low. Their lawyer told me that even if the rent was increased there was no obligation to pay out dividends to the shareholders. I told him I was well aware of that fact but the directors still had a legal obligation to run the company properly. At this point your brother told me that beef and sheep farmers are having a very hard time at the moment. I informed him that I have other clients who are beef and sheep farmers so I am well aware of how sheep farmers are faring.

"Various resolutions were passed," Mr Dockerill continued, "and I voted against them all, but of course I was totally out-voted as everyone else voted in favour of the resolutions."

"Did you tell them what you thought the rent should be?"

"No, no, no," he said emphatically, "I wouldn't do that. We wait for them to suggest a rent then we negotiate. That's how it's done."

"I suppose that makes more sense," I said, trying to imply that I completely understood the logic of what he had said.

"The thing we really have to hammer away at is the rent. I'm sure their lawyer will advise them that there is no way they can legally justify such a low rent and they are not carrying out their duties as directors. If they did go to court they wouldn't have a leg to stand on."

"I don't want to get involved with lawyers."

A couple of weeks later a letter arrived from the surveyor:

To whom it may concern.

It is my opinion as auctioneer and valuer that the property and lands which extend to 357 acres of arable land and 53 acres of woodland at Torlochan farm, -------, if this property was coming up for rent, that it would be worth £5,640 per annum rent.

Again I phoned Mr Dockerill.

"It seems incredibly low after what Rose told me about property prices. It's valued at less than it was eight years ago. It just refers to the land and properties. Could this only refer to the agricultural properties, the barns and tractor sheds and not the residential properties?"

"It should include the dwellings; they are included in the lease. I could write to the surveyor and ask if this valuation takes account of the dwellings."

The answer was pre-empted by an invitation to an AGM along with the next set of accounts, four months after the last AGM.

The rent had been reduced to £1,500 per annum and then withdrawn as a management fee and the farm had been revalued at over £1,000,000.

I was back on the phone to Mr Dockerill. "What is going on?"

"This is quite often done when a company wishes to borrow money. It may well be that your brother is borrowing money on the strength of the value of his shares in Torlochan Farm Ltd."

"He can borrow money until his heart's content so long as it doesn't affect me. Could you attend the AGM as my proxy again?"

"An AGM should be held every year. That's what annual stands for, not after four months."

"This is a facet of my brother's character I am just learning about; he likes holding AGMs."

"Obviously. I'm sure you've picked up the fact that the rent has been reduced back to £1,500. Why go to the trouble of employing a surveyor if they just ignore his recommendations? Paying a rent of £1,500 only to withdraw the same amount for management fees, for doing what?"

"Holding lots of AGMs?"

"Well I can't think he does much else for it. I think the first thing to do is to write to the lawyers, ask why the rent has been reduced instead of increased. The fact that they've given you so much notice makes me think they want you to attend the meeting."

"Perhaps they are going to make me an offer for my shares?"

"It must be a great irritation to your brother that you hold these shares and he can't wind up the company."

"It's a matter of irritation to me as well."

The rental figure from £4,500 charged in the accounts reduced a year later to £1,500 is simply a reflection of both the uncertainty and the unprofitability of farming, which is borne out in the accounts. The letter from the lawyer explained.

"No lawyer would write such a letter; he must only be carrying out your brother's instructions. Mr MacKenzie is blatantly not acting as a director on behalf of the shareholders, namely you."

"What do you suggest I do?"

"Don't threaten to involve lawyers, it makes you look weak. If you offer to sell him your shares, it puts you in a weak position again. I'd leave it. He's going to want your shares, wait for him to make the first move."

"That's my gut feeling as well."

"They've also written asking if I'm going to attend the AGM. I can't see the point considering the way they've totally disregarded everything we agreed over the rent. I won't bother replying. I'll just let them stew."

"What if they are considering making an offer for my shares?"

"It won't make any difference, if they want to make an offer for your shares they can still write to you. It's probably only a matter of time before you hear from them."

So I waited.

Chapter 21

Now that the story has slipped into history, I sometimes talk of that era dispassionately. How could I have been so stupid to trust my mother when she was completely under Rory's influence? I don't suppose my story is terribly original, but I find it a useful anecdote for the children when I'm being sanctimonious.

"You see how important it is to be honest with money. If only your grandmother had been honest with us we would still see her. I want nothing to do with people who aren't honest with money."

When friends ask, 'Do you not even write to her occasionally?' I reply 'Only if the letter's been past an accountant or lawyer first.'

Greg's solution was more pragmatic than mine. He marshalled the facts and presented them in terms of a mathematical problem. His analysis was founded on mathematical equations, based on the theory of probability. One has the theorem, the definition, the core, the half-stops and arrows. The mathematical functions, formalising this logic for the less logical into a definition of logic. He explained it to me like this.

A lot of mathematical problems are proved by contradiction. The refusal of my mother to state, despite repeated requests, that she didn't consider me greedy or selfish and that I hadn't made funny phone calls to Rory's father-in-law, proves that she believes I was and I did. To prove this, assume that she believes these two statements are false. This means that she believes that we are not selfish and greedy, and that I didn't make the funny phone call to Rory's father-in-law. If therefore she believes the statements are false she would say so. Despite repeated requests she has not stated they are false, so she must believe they are true. You see it is as simple as that to a mathematician. You take the formula off the shelf and apply it to your own domestic purposes. This language of patterns had the answer.

So simple. I couldn't even start to rival that logic.

So why, when the annual accounts arrived, did I ask Greg hopefully, "Do you think they send the accounts to keep in touch with me?"

"No, they're just complying with the law. They didn't enclose a note enquiring after your well-being, did they?"

I laugh at my stupidity; Greg doesn't see the funny side. To him it's a sadness.

Over the years, snippets of information concerning my family had filtered down through friends and in-laws, since, for want of a better word, our separation. A friend's mother had played against my mother in a curling match. Rory had been caught speeding at 95 m.p.h. One Christmas I received a card from Susanna; she and her four children were returning to Scotland, but what the card really told me was that she was no longer living with Dennis. I didn't know Fay was married until I read of her divorce; she'd married a television producer, well enough known to deserve a mention in the gossip columns when the marriage hit the rocks. I heard him talking on a chat show several months after the divorce, a queer sensation to hear my ex brother-in-law that I'd never met talking on the radio. The priest factory, as it was irreverently referred to, had long since closed and was now another ubiquitous country house hotel.

Rose told me Elizabeth was doing great things in the horsy world, having won various equestrian events. The really surprising gossip came from Ursula's family. I wonder if it had ever occurred to her that daughters could be an embarrassment. Hazel, Ursula's eldest daughter and her partner had grown marijuana in their back garden, £60,000 worth of the stuff, which they claimed was for their own consumption. The police wouldn't wear it, neither did the courts. They were both jailed for nine months. One thing I remembered about Ursula, she had always been adamant that one must observe the law. She had been a rebel, but always within the boundaries of the law. How did Ursula handle it? She supported her daughter in court, visited her in prison and organised the wedding for Hazel and her partner on their release. She was there for her every inch of the way.

The story that upset me most was learning that George Cramer's road haulage business had gone bust owing debts of four million pounds; whether they ever employed Henry I don't know.

Rose came to stay with us every July on her way to France to visit her parents and sister. We'd take her for a walk by the river or visit a garden, and the following morning she'd continue her journey. While I'd been collecting Alex from a friend's house after our walk, Rose surprised Greg by mentioning my mother.

"Mrs Mackenzie is upset at not seeing Jenny."

"I think she knows what she has to do before any progress can be made."

"She says she won't apologise; if she does it'll just stir things up again."

Rose had also asked if we'd thought about what would happen when my mother died.

"Does she think we are stupid?" I asked

"I told her of course we've thought of that, and I pointed out you're not immortal either. She suggested you just see her once a year. I told her you were either in the family or out of the family and that arrangement was not acceptable."

Dear Jenny,

Last night I had my annual chat with Rose. As usual she gave me good news of you all.

She also said that perhaps now we could think of making a new start and letting bygones be bygones. I had been thinking of visiting Ann Jones in Oxford sometime. Her eldest son Timothy lives in Henley and I am sure she could drop me off for a visit one weekend and pick me up again! Perhaps an hour or two one Sunday? What do you think? I'll wait for your answer before I get in touch with her.

Love to you all.

Jane.

"What exactly did you say to Rose?" I asked Greg angrily.

"I told her you wouldn't consider seeing your mother unless she apologised to you."

"That's not the message that's got through to my mother."

"It's like Chinese whispers. I say you might consider seeing her if she apologises and Rose says you might consider seeing her."

"My mother's told everyone how grasping and selfish I am, how I'd do anything for money. People will be wondering. Surely a greedy daughter would play her cards properly and keep in with a wealthy widowed mother, think of all the money that would go her way when she dies. As long as I don't see her it makes her look bad, as soon as I meet up with her it makes me look bad, the suspicion being I'm after her money. I'll write and tell I can't see her."

Dear Jenny,

First of all I consider myself a great friend and I'm writing because I would love you and your whole family to get back together.

Regarding your mother, she has phoned me annually just to ask how you are and I have not dissuaded her from phoning. I am just a slight link for her to you. She said she was devastated by what had happened and I said that you were too. Now I wonder whether I was wrong. Your mum isn't getting any younger. But maybe you think, so what, she can drop dead for all I care.

Your mum phoned to say that she had written a letter and it had not gone down well. She is distraught at having no contact with you. I don't think of myself as a great peace negotiator but it would be nice if you met your mum again.

I felt I had to write to you as a friend and someone on your side. Don't tear the letter up. Please read it through twice. I won't ever mention it again.

Love,

Rose.

"A great friend she says. I didn't think Rose was so stupid. Where does she get this remark 'so what, she can drop dead for all I care'?"

"You know who that comes from."

"We've always tried to behave properly so that no one could throw that sort of allegation at us, and now a so-called friend writes a phrase like this. How could she?"

"I find it hard to believe she thinks this."

"Perhaps she doesn't but she saw fit to repeat it. I discover my oldest friend has been colluding behind my back with my mother, when she knows exactly how things are between us."

"It's a pretty ham-handed attempt at being a peacemaker."

"You know last year, when Rose insisted on photographing us all, the thought went through my mind. *Were these pictures for her or my mother?* I dismissed the thought as stupid paranoia."

"I'm going to phone your mother. I want to find out where this remark came from."

"I'm not stopping you, but take the phone up to the attic; I don't want the children hearing you having a screaming match with my mother."

Five minutes later he was back in the kitchen. "We should have phoned her years ago. I don't know why I ever wasted so much of my time trying to think of a solution to this impasse. She's not going to change her opinion of us."

"What happened?"

"It started off as a warm friendly conversation, quite pleasant. I told her about Rose's letter and the remark she'd made about not caring if your mother dropped down dead. I told her you'd never wished such a thing and asked if the remark had come from her. She denied it and said she couldn't believe Rose would write such a thing. She more or less admitted that she had tried to deceive us. She explained that she had been overwhelmed by grief after your father died and she didn't know what she was doing. I said we would certainly accept that explanation. Then she seemed to backtrack. She told me I was greedy, well not in so many words. She said the row was about money, and I said no, it was about deception."

"It was about deception over money."

"She was adamant 'everything is about money with you two. It's always was and it always will be'. She also said you were still in her will."

"You didn't raise the matter of her will did you?" I asked, aghast.

"No I never mentioned it. I was surprised she did; it shows you the way her mind works. She said she was only concerned for your happiness and she hadn't written you out of her will. She said she felt as though we'd walked all over her emotions with tackity boots."

"Tackity boots?" I repeated.

"Yes, you know, boots with tacks sticking out of them. I said I was amazed she hadn't put a stop to all this years ago and asked how we were going to resolve the situation, because I couldn't see what I could do to help. Her answer was 'I've got a new life now.' She's caused all this trouble, ruined your friendship with Rose, and then she tells me she's got a new life. I told her not to contact us again, and she said 'Yes and goodbye'."

"I want nothing to do with Rose either. This time I'm going to phone her, there will be no misunderstandings. I'll scream at her and tell her exactly what I think. I'll never call her a friend again, never."

Dear Rose,

I was upset to receive your recent letter, in particular your comment that I could not care less if my mother dropped down dead. As God is my witness I have never wished my mother dead, have no reason to wish my mother dead and I have never referred to my mother in this language.

Because of possible misunderstandings Greg finally phoned my mother to talk to her, the first time either of us has spoken to her in ten years. The situation is just as we had inferred, but now we have it directly from my mother. She does consider us greedy. She is obsessed by the idea that we only want to see her for her money. Obviously I have no desire to see her when she is like this. At the same time I want to tell you that my feelings for my mother are a million miles from 'I could not care less if my mother dropped down dead'.

Although you may never raise the subject of my mother again I shall always know what you are thinking. You have been a very good friend over the years and I am sure you have always acted with the best of intentions, but I do not want to see you ever again. It is upsetting for me to have final proof of what my mother truly believes about me.

I hope that you understand my position and that you will forgive me.

With my best wishes always.

Jenny.

Chapter 22

Dear Jenny,

You will no doubt get a surprise to hear from me, but I thought you would want to know that Aunt Barbara died a few weeks ago. She was always very fond of you and I think you were of her.

She had become very frail over the last couple of years. On her 70th birthday last October I gave her a private concert from a cellist friend – just her, Aunty Fiona, me and the cellist – and she loved it.

At Christmas we were told by her wonderful nurse that her kidneys were failing and before New Year she died very peacefully. We buried her with Granny and Granddaddy. The care she had at the hospital could not have been believed and she also had the support of her Church over many years.

I hope you and your family are all well. Mine flourish. Hazel and Stephanie are both married with three children apiece. They both live about half an hour's drive from me so I am very lucky – Aunty Fiona has grandchildren in New Zealand and Devon.

With love

Aunty Ursula.

"I don't know what to make of it."

"Take the letter at face value," Greg said. "She's just being thoughtful."

"Thoughtfulness was never her thing."

"You should write and thank her. Perhaps she's mellowing in her old age and trying to mend bridges."

"Excuse me if I mix my metaphors, but too much water has gone under this bridge, it's not up for mending. I don't want to open lines of communication with any member of my family."

"Maybe she's more sympathetic towards you than you imagine. It's a pleasant letter, she's not mentioned your mother nor is she asking for a reply. Just send a note acknowledging you've received it."

So I grieved for an aunt who I thought had died years ago, and wrote to one with whom I'd never communicated.

As the years went by the annual accounts from Torlochan worsened, until the partnership stopped paying any rent at all to the company and a loan appeared - interest free. I wrote to my mother. Shouldn't they be charging interest on a loan?

It was repayable on demand. Also it was only a small loan and interest rates were low, therefore it didn't matter if no interest was paid, she wrote in reply.

I wrote to her again. All loans were repayable on demand but I'd never heard of an interest-free loan. I wondered where I could get one. This time she ignored my letter.

Years went by and the loan from the company to the partnership rose and so did interest rates, but still no interest rate was charged.

One boring November day, in sleuth mode, I searched for Torlochan Farms on the Internet. Their business was 'Development and sale of real estate'. Flabbergasted I phoned the Scottish land registry to enquire how much land they'd sold. They hadn't sold land. They'd bought two plots. Also Burnside and the adjoining land had been transferred to Henry, less than three weeks after my father had died. While I had believed my mother wanted to involve me in the family she was already excluding me.

I phoned Stirling council. Rory was in the process of converting the old coach house into three houses and he had already built two new houses and converted a barn. Suddenly everything made sense. The farm had been re-valued so Rory could borrow money against his shares to develop the properties. When I'd discovered Rory had plans to build a house years ago I thought I'd put the kybosh on his enterprise. The houses were already up and running as a holiday rental business at that time.

I wrote to my mother expressing my concern that the company appeared to be charging a rent which was way below the market rates and then allowing the partnership to increase its interest free-loan to the company, instead of paying a rent. (I didn't mention the dwellings.)

She was certain I was aware farming incomes had reduced in relative terms over the last decade. Therefore they cannot justify any alteration in the present arrangements. Perhaps I should look at my shares as an investment for the next generation. (She didn't mention the dwellings either.)

I wrote again asking for the rent to be assessed by an independent expert. The current rent represents a return of around 0.5% per annum which must be well below what would be considered a fair rent by any reasonable person.

She'd discussed my letter at length with Jack and Elizabeth. They agreed with her that there was not much point in asking an independent surveyor to comment on the rent as in the New Year a new farm scheme comes out: one of the features is that tenants may not need to pay rent to landlords - indeed the landlords may have to pay them to farm in an environmentally suitable way. (Still no mention of the dwellings.)

I wrote a third time, hardly able to credit what she'd written. *Your opinion is that the rent is already too high and could be zero or even negative. If this is the case I cannot understand your reluctance in appointing an independent surveyor. The fair rent is a matter of fact which can easily be established. I would jump at the opportunity to rent the land and properties on these terms, if only the directors would make me the offer.*

She wrote back informing me again that the present rent was far too high and did I realise that I was the only other shareholder in Torlochan besides Rory. He has 92% of the shares and would not countenance a rent review.

No mention of the dwellings and such arrogance towards the other shareholder! That did it. I'd bring matters to a head and take it to lawyers.

Greg said I should try to forget it. I thought there would never be a better time to involve lawyers. His idea of lawyers was huge legal bills. If I left it much longer it may be too late.

Mr Dockerill recommended a lawyer in Edinburgh. I contacted David Gibson and told him of the situation. I didn't want to get embroiled in an expensive legal suit but I wanted a resolution if that was possible?

A week later he phoned me back. He'd spoken to his cousin Will Dockerill. I had a very strong case.

As he put it: "Your mother and your brother have manipulated affairs in such a way that the balance sheet does not represent a fair indication of the company's assets, and they have restricted the profits by the amount of rent payable by the tenants (themselves)."

He thought the best course would be for him to phone Rory's lawyer, explain that we intended to take Rory and my mother to court for oppression of minorities. Apparently the law took a very dim view of this offence. He didn't like using threats but he could see no alternative.

Countless letters flew from lawyer to lawyer with Rory dragging his heels at every opportunity. David recommended that I appoint a surveyor, Robert Hill, who specialised in disputes over agricultural property. He would carry out a detailed survey to calculate the value of my shares. I spoke to Robert, giving details of what I knew, the type of land, the bed and breakfast business, the four houses they rented out and the coach house, which was being converted into three more properties.

Robert phoned me the day after his appointment at Torlochan. Rory was doing pretty well out of the company. There were actually five houses rented out; we hadn't been aware the old stable near to the main farmhouse was converted into a three-bedroomed dwelling. Each property was rented out at an annual rent of between seven to nine thousand pounds. Rory had been exceptionally helpful, lending him an umbrella and showing him around. He'd walked around the farm and seen an impressive herd of beef cows. Normally he wouldn't have expected a cup of tea, given the circumstances. However Phillipa had laid on a lunch for him, and a charm offensive by the sound of things. She'd explained how unfair the situation was. Rory had taken the financial pain to develop the properties, thereby improving the value of my shares.

What a conundrum for him! Fine, I didn't deny that he'd spent his own money doing up the properties, but then why hadn't the expenses gone through the company accounts and more to the point, where were the rental payments from the tenants? This could only mean that the accounts which he'd sent me over the years, which he'd signed off as being true, were in fact false, casting grave doubts on his suitability as a director. Poor soul, he was on a sticky wicket, and that's what I suspect his lawyer had told him.

Greg drafted a letter and sent it to David, who tweaked it with legal jargon, and forwarded it to Rory's lawyer to pass on to Rory:

I confirm that I have now received the Report from my expert in connection with the valuation of Torlochan Farm. I enclose a copy of this valuation.

My client has given consideration to this valuation, and I am entirely satisfied, as indeed is she, that her position as a minority shareholder has been significantly oppressed by the conduct on the part of the partners and the Directors of the Company over the years. Accordingly on that basis I enclose a copy schedule showing the basis of my client's claim.

Clearly my client's preference would be to dispose of her shareholdings on an agreed valuation to your clients, but you will appreciate, in light of the advice now received, that the proposed figure of £2,500 made previously for the purchase of the shares is wholly and utterly inadequate.

Notwithstanding that, my client is anxious that negotiations should proceed in early course with a view to endeavouring to reach agreement so that she may dispose of her shareholding in the company. Clearly, if that is not possible, the only remedy then left available to her is to Petition the Court alleging oppression in respect of her minority shareholding. She does hope, however, that this will not be necessary and that matters can be resolved amicably.

Oppression of the minority Shareholder.

I have enclosed a schedule which I have drawn up to demonstrate how the rents shown in the company accounts, as payable, compare with the rents which should have been paid, according to the information provided by Mr Hill, the surveyor. It should be noted that, although the rents payable are low, the accounts show that even these amounts have not been fully paid. Instead they are shown as accruals, to the extent that in the present accounts there is a loan outstanding from the company to the partnership of £37,429, on which the company is receiving no interest.

The shortfall between the rents paid (less payments to the directors) and the rent which should have been paid is effectively a loan from the company to the partnership. Allowing for interest on the loan at base rate plus 2%, which is a modest rate for a bank loan, the outstanding rent is £243,280.

In his letter of 13th October the surveyor advised me that if the lease between the company and the partnership had been drawn up on a commercial basis then the rent would currently be around £50,000 per annum.

The rent has been ridiculously low for the last sixteen years. It is clear to me that the directors have a hopeless conflict of interest through their interest in the partnership and have not been treating my client fairly as a minority shareholder. They have treated the assets of the company as if these were exclusively their property. For example,

a)   On a regular basis they have drawn a salary while not paying my client a dividend. This appears to me a back door method of paying themselves a dividend while denying my client one.

b)   The rent is very low even on the basis of the current lease. If the directors were running the company fairly they would have replaced the old lease with a proper lease, as outlined by the surveyor in his letter.

The loss in rent, plus a reasonable allowance for interest at base rate plus 2%, is currently £243,280. If the lost rent had been assessed properly on an 'arm's length' basis then the loss would be much bigger than shown above. For instance, for last year alone, the surveyor has assessed the market rent as around £50,000, compared to the £15,500 on the basis of the out-of-date lease.

The way forward:

a) *The partnership should pay the company a sum of £243,280 for the lost rent plus interest.*

b) *A proper lease should be drawn up between the company and the partnership, as outlined by the surveyor in his letter, and the future rent raised to £50,600 per annum.*

c) *The directors, who are also partners in A&J Mackenzie, have a hopeless conflict of interest and should resign as directors of the company to be replaced by independent directors.*

As an alternative, and this is a much preferred option, the company should make an offer for my client's shares. The value of my client's shareholding of 8% of the company is £150,000

I accordingly await hearing from you, and confirm that this letter is written entirely without prejudice to my client's whole rights and pleas in respect of any subsequent proceedings, without any admission of liability whatever, and is not to be founded upon any circumstances in any subsequent court proceedings.

Yours sincerely,

David Gibson.

I don't know if the letter scared Rory but it scared me and I was sending it.

Dear David,

I have today met with my client to discuss your letter. My client informed me that he has instructed his own independent valuation of the estate and I shall revert to you just as soon as this has been obtained

Kind regards,

Emily.

And along with this was a covering letter from David indicating he would expect some progress within four to six weeks and I was to phone him if I hadn't heard from him in this time.

It looked as though Rory was squaring up for a battle and this was the last thing I wanted. I was in two minds whether to tell Greg about this latest letter. Pension funds had taken a hammering and he had a portfolio of unhappy clients. To make matters worse, Fields, the company he worked for was on the verge of being taken over by a large multinational; the venture capitalists who owned Fields wanted their money out. Greg, now fifty, was concerned he would have trouble finding another position. Did he really need this added strain first thing on a Saturday morning? Coming into the kitchen for his breakfast he appeared pretty relaxed, despite the stress he was under. Was it mean of me to mention the letter when he seemed in good spirits and ruin his weekend? On the other hand, if I bottled the information up I'd worry like anything and ruin my weekend. Blow it, I'd tell him.

"We've received a letter from David Gibson," I said, handing it to him, and turned back to the oven busying myself as I continued to cook the breakfast.

He scanned it.

"This is a positive start to the New Year." I hated it when he was sarcastic. I never knew how to handle things when he was like this. I turned the sausages over and tried to look unconcerned, but my toes were curling up in my slippers. I realised I should have at least waited until after we'd eaten before giving him the letter. I could cope with his irritation at my brother's behaviour more easily when I wasn't hungry.

"Of course I'm not pleased. The thought of fighting this out in court bothers me."

"That was my nightmare as well; he'd just ignore our letters as he constantly has done in the past and we'd be forced to take him to court, but now he's playing our game."

"He's getting his own surveyor, which means he doesn't accept our surveyor's report," I pointed out.

"It means he is taking us seriously at last, he's negotiating with us. This is what I would expect his lawyer to recommend. She'll have warned him that, at any time, he could be summoned to court and that we have a very strong case. She has advised him to appoint his own surveyor so they can negotiate us down a couple of thousand pounds and justify her huge fees. You didn't expect him just to roll over and pay what we asked for? David Gibson's very good. He has kept the pressure on and put the wind up them."

"Why didn't David say it was good news in his letter then?"

"He probably thought he didn't have to."

I looked up at him from where I stood next to the oven, watching him reread the letter with relief on his face.

"Just what we need then, some good news," I said adding: "with lawyers involved their surveyor can't possibly fail to include the new houses and barn conversions the way Nick Smith did so many years ago."

This time, unbelievably, Rory's surveyor estimated the rental value of Torlochan at £6,500 per annum, less than it had been eighteen years ago when my father had been alive and there were no houses rented out. Rory had employed another crony happy to do his bidding and assess a ludicrously low rental. How could the surveyor possibly defend that rent if it came to court? I felt like phoning the man up to ask if there was a typo on his report or was he just incompetent? Except I didn't. Their lawyer's covering letter, as expected, claimed that our assessed rental was too high, and had left it at that with no counter-proposal offered.

Rather than spend time and money deliberating over a rent that was clearly absurd, David asked them to put forward a valuation of my shares as a basis for settlement.

The ball was back in Rory's court, we'd have to wait. A month later with still no response I phoned David and asked him to send Rory a second letter, explaining that Rory usually needed a 'bit of a kick' before there was any reaction.

Dear Emily,

My client is not willing to allow this matter to drift indefinitely and, unless I hear from you by the end of this month, my instructions are simply to proceed to raise proceedings. I do hope, however, that this will not be necessary.

Kind regards,

David.

I read the letter. It took my breath. The words were catapulting me headlong into a courtroom and that was the last thing I wanted. I winced as I reread the letter to Greg. "This wasn't the 'bit of a kick' I had in mind. I wouldn't have had the nerve to consent to this letter, and what if Rory recognizes we are just calling his bluff."

"David probably thought Rory would happily go on ping-ponging letters backwards and forwards indefinitely if he didn't get a rocket," Greg said. "We have to trust him; he must have a feel for the situation talking to Rory's lawyer, and the fact that Rory hasn't responded most likely means he knows he's on the back foot."

The response was remarkably speedy. An email arrived confirming they would be in touch shortly with their valuation for my shares. David was concerned that matters were drifting. Though I had no intention of taking legal action, I'd go along with the pretence; it seemed to be getting them moving, even if it was slowly. Could David send an email that I had agreed to defer action for two weeks.

The weeks dragged on and on and still no offer arrived. Greg was going to a conference in Edinburgh, he arranged to stay on for an extra day to meet David and consider how to proceed, if at all. David assured him 'it is highly unusual for the number of dwellings currently owned by Torlochan Farms to remain within an agricultural lease. In his opinion it would have been normal practice in a situation of this kind for the surplus, secondary dwellings not occupied by agricultural employees to have been separately let out by the landowner to the tenants on a short assured tenancy agreement'.

Greg returned to Henley fired up with the knowledge that we were pursuing a criminal act and the only way forward now was through the courts.

"I thought we'd agreed we wouldn't take it to court if the sabre-rattling didn't work."

"Can you imagine the chairman of Tesco building a store with his own money, marketing it as a Tesco store and keeping all the proceeds for himself? He'd end up in the nick and that's what Rory has done with Torlochan."

"Everyone knows how fickle the courts are; there's no guarantee we'd win," I said.

"We've spent a lot of time and money on this business, we might as well see it out to the end." Somewhere along the way there had been a role-reversal. "Especially," he added, "as we have an extremely strong case. Rory's antics amount to fraud. I know there is a slight possibility we might lose, but it's worth the risk."

David briefed an advocate on our behalf, Fergus MacKee. The cost was frightening and, once we'd started the proceedings, we could not withdraw unless we met all Rory's expenses as well as our own. After months of tedious form-filling and email correspondence a date was set for the court hearing. Greg flew to Scotland with me. The thought of standing in the witness box terrified me, I needed him for moral support.

Waiting in the foyer of the court for David and Fergus to arrive we watched armies of bald men (perhaps it's because they're in deep denial that advocates wear wigs in court) moving around decisively, busy looking important and intimidating. They didn't give the impression of being a sensitive bunch, as they cast looks of deep suspicion in my direction on their march past towards the courtroom, preparing for the kill. Well, I suppose they'd cut their teeth on murder cases, GBH clients, sinister Mafia types sparring in underworld feuds.

David and Fergus turned up shortly after us and we were ushered into a small conference room. Fergus appeared bemused by the case. The crime in question might not be a moment of great legal history to him, but to me it was a terrifying experience. My mouth had gone dry, I could feel the blood pounding through the back of my neck, and my forehead was sweating. My body was preparing for battle and I wasn't even in the courtroom yet, let alone standing in the witness box. He quizzed me as though he couldn't understand the point of the dispute and was struggling to understand the information for the first time. I answered his questions, trying to sound neutral, while inside I felt decidedly hysterical. We're paying all this money just so he can act stupid instead of being of assistance to me. Hadn't David briefed him? Of course I knew he had. Fergus was only giving me a taste of what to expect in court and I really didn't relish the prospect of being served up to the judge like this. He asked my permission to negotiate an out-of-court settlement with Rory's advocate and I agreed. The lawyers went out, leaving Greg and me alone.

"Why am I doing this? I've never felt so stressed in my life."

"We knew it wasn't going to be easy," Greg said. "We're on the final lap; we just have to stick with it."

"It's only money - we can survive with what we've got. Why are we doing this? If it goes against us it'll be disaster but if it goes against them Elizabeth can easily bail them out. £100,000 is just small fry for her."

After a nerve-wracking forty minutes David returned to the room. Would we accept an out of court settlement? Rory was prepared to offer me £71,000 for my 8% of Torlochan and pay my legal expenses; he considered this a generous offer. So did I. Having discussed it at length with Greg, I'd decided to accept £50,000. I had even decided just to take £40,000 if that was their offer, for it was a reasonable bung by most people's standards. But with £71,000 we could pay off our mortgage and have money left over for a little fling.

David thought we could push for a further £15-£20,000. As it was, I couldn't believe my luck and I didn't have the heart for more arguments over money. I just wanted the business wound up. Thanking the lawyers we bundled ourselves into a taxi in a state of mild euphoria and headed for the airport, hugely relieved at having played the end game with more success than we'd dreamt of. The final tie with my family, cut at last.

Chapter 23

"Hello Jenny, you don't know of my existence and I know so much about you. My name is Grace Mackenzie, we're sisters-in-law."

I sat down in amazement. "Are we?"

"Yes, for almost three years now."

There is a charm in the Irish accent, the gentle lilt, so close to singing. In this voice there was more, magnetism in the warmth, inviting me to listen. For years I'd been dreading this phone call, I knew what it was about, but I could not be rude to such a kind voice.

She told me how she'd come to Glasgow to escape an unhappy marriage, swearing she would never marry again, and threw herself into her work. She was a psychiatric nurse and Barbara had been one of her patients.

I wasn't interested in a potted history of her life, but I hadn't the nerve to say anything.

There had been a great rapport between them; they both loved music and crosswords, although Barbara had been much better at crosswords than she'd ever be. She'd been with Barbara when she died, attended her funeral and afterwards been invited back to Burnside. That was when she'd met Henry.

"He's the kindest man I know and he makes me laugh, but I didn't want another husband."

"Why did you marry him then?" It was of no concern to me, I was procrastinating. Fearful of when she was going to bring up the true reason for her phone call - my mother.

"I'm several years older than Henry; I thought I was just going through the change. I was almost five months pregnant when I discovered I was expecting a baby. I was so angry I refused to talk to Henry for almost a month. It's a terrible thing to say, but I wanted to lose the baby. Sometimes I look at her now and can't believe I didn't want her."

"When was she born?" I was still playing for time, preparing myself for what was to come. I felt sick.

"On our honeymoon." Despite myself I giggled. Then it came, what I had been dreading.

"Your mum had a stroke last week and another one last night. I'm sorry Jenny, but it's not looking at all good. All your family are here, at Burnside, but it's you she wants to see. She keeps crying and asking one of us to contact you. She's never mentioned you until the last couple of days and now she talks of nothing else."

"Do you think my mother likes me?"

A silence. After all the garrulous talk the silence seemed to last an age. I waited for her answer, then it came, quietly embarrassed, spoken deliberately.

"I think if she liked you she would not have treated you the way she did."

"Why are you phoning me then? What's your motive?"

"There is no motive, it's just that she's been asking all day to see you and none of your brothers or sisters would phone you. It breaks my heart - she's desperate to see you. I told her I would ask you to come and see her. I know what she did was wrong, but she doesn't deserve to die like this."

"What is she expecting, a deathbed repentance?" I said, trying to keep the contempt out of my voice.

"She just wants to see you one last time."

It felt like a command I'd been expecting, one that natural decency refused to let me ignore. In my mind I'd been here a hundred times. Hadn't I given her a full explanation in writing of why we would never meet again?

Despite everything, I knew Greg would tell me to go. Bugger him! Why should I show her any kindness? Could it be a mortal sin to withhold the last request of a dying parent? There was no one I could ask and all the time I was wondering how I could live with myself if it was. I didn't want to hate myself for not going. I could feel myself caving in.

"I suppose I should show some mercy; she is my mother after all," I said.

"It will make your mum very happy."

I wasn't going all that way to make her happy or to show mercy. The truth was, I couldn't stand the thought of spending the rest of my life scratching uncomfortably under a hair shirt. I was going for my own mental well-being; terrified that if I didn't go there'd be some awful retribution. Why, why, why did she always win, always have the last word?

"I'll come up today," I added reluctantly. "Although I doubt I'll arrive before early evening. I'll phone you when I reach Glasgow."

It was a beautiful day to be taking such a journey and normally I'd have gazed out of the window and marvelled at the countryside. Instead, all the time I was thinking of my mother. In the cold clarity of the northern light I felt a curious, grudging admiration creeping into my sympathies towards her. With a new awareness of her predicament I saw her in a fresh, impartial light. As a gamekeeper understands the adroitness of a poacher, I thought of her cunning and was amazed at the nerve involved in attempting such deceit. I had never failed to be astonished by her ability to execute perverse arguments which somehow sanitised the nature of her duplicity. My mother was like a defence barrister in a despicable fraud case. Whilst not insensitive to the moral depravity involved, her prime concern was to convince the jury there was no case. The exercise was her sole mission. With the barrister's skill and zeal, my mother had argued on her son's behalf, knowing the risk she was taking, a calculated risk that had gone awry.

Always one step ahead of me, she had the advantage when her misdeed was disclosed. Like the poacher, she put up a stout, almost commendable defence, with the confidence of one that feels respected and appreciated as a folk hero. I, the gamekeeper, was always one step behind, having to tread carefully, for the defence had been well prepared, all the ground-work had been covered while I slept in innocence.

As a clever hunter corners its prey, she'd lined up the opposition against me. Relying on the kind support of her sisters, the indiscriminate loyalty and devotion of her sons and other daughters and the recognition that the lawyers had completed their legal obligation. Like all the best laid plans, there had been an element of risk, calculated risk, but they should have known me better - I didn't conform to their expectations.

The state of British Railways meant that my arrival in Glasgow was three hours later than planned. There was no shortage of taxis waiting to ferry the travellers to their destinations. My driver looked delighted when I gave him the address. He consulted a little directory of prices and announced "Thirty-five pounds."

With a beating heart I climbed in and phoned Burnside to let them know I was on my way, praying that Rory would not answer. It was Grace. She sounded relieved to hear my voice.

"The others will be leaving very soon. Henry and I will be the only two here when you arrive." *Thank goodness,* I thought.

In the dark, the journey out to the farm seemed to take forever, and all the time I was thinking of what to say. What could I say? I felt sick with worry. How could I have forgotten the letter Greg and I had taken such pains to write for just such an occasion?

For the last few miles I was obliged to give directions, and then at the T-junction I saw the large Bed and Breakfast sign, Torlochan Farmhouse, with an arrow underneath.

"That's it," I pointed out, and slumped back, unable to say another word.

The farm road was a lot more pot-holed than I remembered. I heard the driver cursing under his breath, as he drove at a snail's pace. At last we arrived; I paid him and climbed out onto the gravel path leading up to the house. I felt sick. What had I done? It was idiotic to feel honour-bound to see her. I owed her nothing. What was I hoping for? I turned round, determined now to go back to Glasgow. Too late, the taxi lights were disappearing down the drive. Stupid man, he could have made another thirty-five pounds if only he'd waited a minute. Now I had no choice; I'd come this far and had no means of escape. I didn't know knees actually shook in times of fear. The door of the house opened and a flood of light poured out into the night. The time had come. What was I going to say?

A big heavy lady hurried down the steps to greet me, with surprising sprightliness. Reaching out both arms she pressed my hand warmly. A few years older than Henry she'd said. What an understatement. The face I looked on was a good few years older than mine. It wore an open, uncomplicated expression.

"I'm glad you've arrived. Your mother had another stroke this afternoon and I think she's holding on just to see you."

There was no need to say anything as she led me up the steps and into the house.

"We're using the study downstairs as her bedroom," she said as she ushered me into the room.

Lifeless she lay there, propped up on three pillows, a washed out ragdoll, strands of limp grey hair glued over her pallid skin, her eyelids closed, as though asleep. I'd been so scared of talking to her; it had never crossed my mind she might actually die before I arrived. I gasped, a sharp rattling noise came out of my throat and for a moment I thought I would laugh at the irony of God's cruel joke, allowing her to die moments before I arrived. Then a wave of relief passed over me, as I sank down in the chair beside her bed, the anxiety melting away. And the thought crossing my mind was, *thank goodness I don't have to talk to her.* All the stupid worrying had been unnecessary.

Grace leaned over and gently shook Mum's arm. Her eyes opened slowly as she turned her head towards me. Staring in disbelief, I said as lightly as I could.

"Hello, I've come to see you."

"Ursula," she murmured with a start.

"No Mum, it's me, Jenny." As I spoke I heard the door close behind me as Grace left the room.

Now it was her turn to stare. "Of course it is, of course it is," she echoed. "How strange, you two could never stand each other and now you look more like Ursula than her own daughters."

"I can assure you it's not through choice." I laughed, removing my glasses.

"Do you know you have beautiful eyes?" she said.

I didn't know what to say. As it was I cried, such a ridiculous remark to cry over, it made me feel stupid, which in turn made the crying worse.

Then through her laboured breathing I heard, "You always cried too much." Admonishing me the way she used to. *Nothing has changed,* I thought.

Her hand slid across the sheet and the knobbly cadaverous fingers grasped mine. She continued with words I'd never expected to hear.

"Can you forgive me? What I did to you was so wrong."

"It doesn't matter. We've all the money we need." It wasn't the time to air grievances.

"I'm not just talking about your father's will. I know I was never very good to you. I never treated you as a mother should treat a daughter. Every morning when I woke up I'd say to myself I must try and be kind to you today, and I meant to, but I just couldn't help myself."

By now the effort of breathing was immense, but after a moment's pause she carried on.

"You were such a difficult, whingeing child. You never played with the other children and your wheezing, your constant wheezing drove me mad. The doctors advised me to ignore you. Your father used to get cross with me, he didn't understand. Perhaps he was right? Maybe if I'd spent more time with you things would have been different. He always blamed me for the way you turned out."

"What's wrong with the way I turned out? I think I'm alright. I've two lovely children, a kind husband in a good job, I like my house and on the whole life's not too bad."

"Real Middle England," she said, and I could still hear it, that disdain for the townie, nothing personal.

"What's so bad about that?"

"So long as you're happy. That's all that matters."

"Yes I am," I assured her.

I heard the door open quietly behind me. Who was it? With dread I looked round. A young man came in sporting an earring and an untidy haircut. I racked my brains. Who could he be? Stretching out his arm we shook hands.

"Dr. Davidson," he said by way of introduction. He looked young enough to be my son.

He spoke to my mother, calling her Jane as he held the stethoscope to her chest and told her what we both knew. Her heart was very weak.

"It's not much longer, I know, but I'm happy to die now I've got my daughter with me."

And her crinkly fingers curled round my hand.

"It's not every mother who's fortunate enough to have a daughter like yours," he said, looking at me as he spoke. If only he knew. Mum and I exchanged meaningful glances. "You would be surprised how many people have no relatives to stay with them at a time like this," he added as he left the room.

"Will you stay with me tonight?" I heard her ask.

"I'll stay with you until the dawn breaks," I promised, squeezing her hand.

"Say a prayer with me Jenny," her voice whispered.

Holding her hand I recited slowly and hesitantly the words from the only prayer I knew, the Lord's Prayer. Was this what she wanted? I wasn't sure. As I stumbled on

"Give us each day our daily bread," I heard her whispering, barely audible, strange guttural sounds.

I stopped for a moment, long enough to catch the words. She was speaking in German. I hardly know the language but I understood the words. I continued "Deliver us from evil . . ." Strange I should have felt so close to her as we spoke together in different languages. I stayed holding her hand. In the stillness of the night, this precious time was ours, mother and daughter. I wouldn't let it go.

Words of forgiveness and understanding were the last she uttered. I don't know when the last breath left her, but in the confusing half-light of the very early morning, I saw a face at peace, a face that looked so gentle. The damp, cold fingers that lay in my hand would not stir again. I lingered in the room alone with her for the last time, her spirit so close, her life gone. I waited, forbidding those long gentle rays of first light, as they coaxed in the dawn I never wanted to see. Out of the receding night I saw, clearly now, the denuded branches of the old chestnut tree silhouetted like filigree against the early morning sky.